THE CALMING, GRATITUDE, AND APPRECIATIVE TECHNIQUES

Book Six of the Twin Brain Self-Help Resource for a fulfilling life and adapting to change

DR. BENALILIGHA FRANCIS SELEMO,
MRS ALICE ENAIKIDIGHA GBEKEBOR FEGBE-OTU
AND MISS ROSELYN ESEITEBAFA SELEMO

DEDICATION

To Mrs Alice Enaikidigha Gbekebor Fegbe-otu, my mum who loves much and sponsored my education to doctorate level.

Authors: Dr. Benaliligha Francis Selemo, Mrs Alice Enaikidigha Gbekebor Fegbe-Otu and Miss Roselyn Eseitebafa Selemo

Twin Brain Ltd
Davenport House,
16 Pepper Street,
Canary Wharf,
London E14 9RP,
United Kingdom.
Email admin@twinbrain.org,
Phone 0333 800 3006, 0333 789 0012.
Website www.twinbrain.org

Editors

▶ Sarah Michie Holds a MA (Hons) in Psychology and a degree in Scots Law London, United Kingdom.

▶ Mohammad Shuja-ul Hoda Cognitive behaviour therapist, interpersonal therapist, and couple therapist London, United Kingdom.

▶ Jacquie Rondon Retired specialist United Kingdom National Health Service (NHS) Cardio-thoracic Senior nurse Intensive care. London,UK.

Book Cover Image- Faith Anne Kasuku, Lead Designer at PHATYDESIGN, Nairobi, Kenya.

Book Cover Design- Faith Anne Kasuku, Lead Designer at PHATYDESIGN, Nairobi, Kenya

Book Interior Images - Salman Shaikh, Lead Designer for Depixed, Ahmedabad, India.

Typesetting and Book Interior Design Faith Anne Kasuku, Lead Designer at PHATYDESIGN, Nairobi, Kenya.

First Published 10 December 2021 by Twin Brain Publishing (trading name for Twin Brain Ltd).

ISBN 978-1-7398056-2-3 (print book). 978-1-7398056-3-0 (e-book).

About This Book and Twin Brain Resources

This book aims to contribute to your understanding of what the Twin Brain is, how it works and if you have one. We hope that our coping techniques in this book, as well as in the Twin Brain web App and Twin Brain mobile App will help you develop self-help coping techniques. Along with the support of trained and accredited professionals, the Twin Brain resources can reduce stress and emotional problems as well as improve your health and well-being.

Disclaimer

The resources of this book, as well as all other materials of the Twin Brain Ltd and its sister organisations do not provide emergency services and MUST NOT be used as an alternative to professional medical advice. You must consult a trained medical professional if you are worried about your health or the health of someone else. Twin Brain Ltd and its entire sister organisations cannot be held liable for the use of its resources.

TABLE OF CONTENTS

Twin Brain Ltd
Davenport House,
16 Pepper Street,
Canary Wharf,
London E14 9RP,
United Kingdom.
Email admin@twinbrain.org
Phone 0333 800 3006, 0333 789 0012.
Website www.twinbrain.org

YOUR SAFETY

Are you feeling suicidal, harming yourself (e.g., pulling hair, cutting, etc), or being bullied, in domestic violence (e.g., abused sexually, financially, verbally, etc) or at risk to another person?

If No You can proceed to other pages of this resource, but you are still advised to keep and use the emergency contact details in this resource.

If Yes

▶ You must contact and receive support from a Helpline you know or from one of the organisations below.

▶ You must contact the crisis help services, your family doctor, your counsellor, a friend, or family member in your country.

▶ You SHOULD ONLY proceed to other pages of this resource when you no longer feel at risk to yourself and/or to other people, including children.

RISK AND EMERGENCY CONTACTS

Note More details on Risk and Emergency Contacts are available towards the end of this book.

For People Living in the United Kingdom

If you are in the UK-and consider yourself to be a risk to yourself or others, please contact

- **Samaritans** 08457909090 (free 24-hour crisis line). www.samaritans.org
- **Saneline** 03003047000, 07984967708 (practical information, crisis care, and emotional support). www.sane.org.uk
- **Your doctor (GP)** If you feel the need to talk to a medical professional, contact your doctor via phone during working hours. You can find your local medical centre at https//www.nhs.uk/service-search/find-a-doctor. You do not need to be registered to make an emergency appointment.
- **Single Point of Access Crisis Helpline** at the place of your residence. This can be found with an online search and is available to provide medical support 24/7.

For People Living in Other Countries

If you are overseas and consider yourself being a risk to yourself or to others, please

- Contact your friends, family members, and your local Accident and Emergency agencies.

SHOULD I ASK FOR MEDICAL HELP?

It is a decision for you and your doctor to make

It is up to you to decide whether you require and need more help after reading and using any of the Twin Brain self-help coping resources. If you are unsure about needing medical assistance, please consult your family doctor.

Where do I get help?

You may develop coping techniques from

- The self-help guides in the Twin Brain Books, Twin Brain web Apps or Twin Brain web Apps. The link to the Twin Brain resources is www.twinbrain.org or www.healthbj-uk.org. These tools do not substitute medical advice and care from a trained medical professional.

- Professional support through your doctor or your professionally trained and accredited local therapist. These medical professionals may charge you a service fee for their treatments using their own techniques, or for assisting you to work through the Twin Brain's self-help coping resources.

A lot of help available

Although we cannot recommend any specific doctor or service, there is a lot of help available:

(i) If you live in the UK you should contact your doctor or local NHS Service. They will tell you on how to get support from a local NHS counsellor or a therapist in the voluntary health sector. Services through the NHS are usually free at point of use, or very low-cost.

(ii) If you live outside the UK and you know how to find an accredited local counsellor or therapist in your country, you should contact them.

(iii) If you live outside the UK and you do not know how to find a trained and accredited local counsellor or therapist in your country, you should contact your local doctor who will explain how to find a suitable professional near yoo.

Remote Options

You can also book remote online, phone, email, texting or video consultations, counselling, or therapy from anywhere in the world. Contact your local family doctor or counsellor for remote support.

Other Options

If you cannot get help locally through your family doctor or counsellor

- You may book remote or face to face sessions at www. healthbj-uk.org, or within the Twin Brain web Apps and mobile Apps at www.twinbrain.org.
- You may also search online for accredited Counsellors or therapists offering remote support.

INTRODUCTION

Welcome to book 6 of the Twin Brain series.

This book may help you to explore and identify available, existing, new, or previously successful best possible solutions, strengths and resources to address a current difficult situation. You are reminded to allow yourself to be thankful for what you have, to appreciate yourself, others, and your environment, to believe and reward yourself, to show compassion and kindness to yourself: to invest in thinking and doing wonderful things for yourself without neglecting people who need you. You are encouraged to practise to create calmness that improves the quality of sleep, reduce anxiety, and reduce the replaying of unhelpful trauma (emotional injuries) memories.

Collectively, the techniques contribute to positive emotions, physical reactions (joy, contentment, calmness, etc.) and the release of happy hormones (serotonin) in your body. Serotonin produces many emotional and medical benefits that include reducing anxiety by producing calmness, and increasing the strength of your immune system, and slowing aging.

Happy reading and please do get in touch to let us know how you got on!

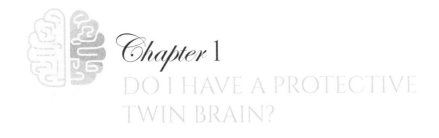

Chapter 1
DO I HAVE A PROTECTIVE TWIN BRAIN?

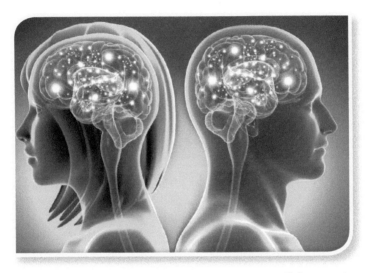

The workings of the human brain remain a possible mystery even to the most advanced of science.

1.1 What is a Twin Brain?

We use the name 'Twin Brain' because:

☐ The human brain behaves like a computer, it captures and stores information as helpful or unhelpful files. These can be essential for our well-being. The stored information can tell us about threats, or what makes us happy. These files can be helpful and have the potential to improve the way we function. However, some of these files can be also corrupted or 'unhelpful' and have the potential to disrupt the way we function. When thinking, some people use unhelpful thinking styles – 'corrupted' brain files. If this way of thinking affects you, your friends, relationships, or colleagues, this can become a problem.

5

How true may this be for you now? If yes, what? If no, why?

☐ The human brain behaves like a computer and can use stored information to help us make decisions. For example, whether to fight or run from threats, or find ways to be happy and creative.

How true may this be for you now? If yes, what? If no, why?

☐ We can take steps to manage our brain 'files' – we can create, install or activate 'helpful' brain files, and un-install, repair or update 'unhelpful' ones, just like you would with documents on a computer. By managing these files, we can be happier and more satisfied with our lives.

Note Further information can be found in the Book, mobile App or web App 'Do I Have a Protective Twin Brain?', which is available at www.twinbrain.org.

1.2 The good news is that

☐ **The Twin Brain is teachable You can 'teach' your Twin Brain** to work with and not against you. This helps your Twin Brain to help you live a fulfilling and satisfying life and protect you against threats and unhelpful thoughts.

☐ You can learn coping techniques to
  ▶ change your way of thinking so it is more helpful to you:
  ▶ change your unhelpful brain files to prevent you from developing unhelpful thinking habits: and
  ▶ activate good brain files to enable you to develop good thinking habits.

6

- 'Unhelpful' brain files, especially simple ones, can be easily changed using thought coping techniques such as a *Thought Court* or the *Thought Record*. Examples of this are provided in the Twin Brain book or App called '*Thoughts Coping Techniques for Simple Brain Files*' or '*More Coping Techniques*', which are available at www.twinbrain.org. You may obtain a Thought Court or Thought Record from your family doctor or local therapist, who may help you learn to learn how to use it.

- You can develop coping techniques through the Twin Brain step-by-step guides or from a trained medical professional.

- **The Twin Brain is teachable**. This means that there are proactive steps that you can take to acquire coping techniques and to manage helpful or unhelpful brain files. You may acquire good new files from other sources, create your own new good files, activate, or enhance your existing good files, increase the use of good files, and improve the creative and resilience functions or duties of your Twin Brain. These other sources may help you to learn, acquire good positive, resilient files from hope-giving friends, family members, or from books (including Holy Faith Books), podcasts, films, religious and faith sermons, workshops, public speeches, stories, counsellors, and therapists in different fields, etc.

1.3 Step By Step Exercise to Identify your Common Corrupted Brain Files.

If you want to know which of your brain files might be corrupted ('unhelpful'), we recommend that you read the book, or the App module titled *'Do I Have a Twin Brain?'* before you start this resource. This contains a list and description of those unhelpful brain files or thinking styles that most people experience. The book or App *'Do I Have a Twin Brain?'* also contains a step-by-step exercise to help you identify your common corrupted brain files.

1.4 What's next?

Now that you have worked through this section, you should pause and reflect on your answers. Put the book or App aside for a few minutes before answering the questions below

☐ What have you learned and achieved from this section?

Example

Some of the thinking I do often is unhelpful, but I learned they are not permanent. I can get assistance to change my unhelpful thinking styles.

_____

_____

_____

☐ What self-help coping techniques do you want to learn?

Example

How to develop helpful thinking styles. Not to worry too much.

_____

_____

_____

☐ Are there any questions you would like to ask medical professionals?

Example

Are there other techniques apart from the Thought Court technique that I can use to change my unhelpful thinking?

_____

_____

_____

☐ What specific self-improvement goal or achievement do you want to set for yourself for the next week?

Example

To go to my nearest shop to buy bread and change my thinking that if I go, every stranger in the shop would be thinking I'm a sore loser.

_____

_____

_____

It may be useful to provide yourself with at least five minutes a week to regularly review and reflect on your self-improvement goal. If you do not set aside time to take care of your wellbeing, the daily demands of life may overwhelm you, and it will become harder to develop self-help techniques.

Do not ignore your well-being because life is not endless here on earth. Try to do at least one small act of kindness, compassion, or self-care for yourself today.

My Review Date _____ **Time** _____ Place _____

1.5 Your Feedback

The Twin Brain Project Team would like to hear from you if you have helpful suggestions that could help them to improve any aspect of this section for other users. Email your suggestions to admin@twinbrain.org. Please copy info@healthbj-uk.org into your email to make sure your feedback is received. Thank you in advance for helping to improve the Twin Brain resource.

Chapter 2
THE CALMING, GRATITUDE, AND APPRECIATIVE TECHNIQUES OVERVIEW

The techniques covered in this book include

- The Appreciative Enquiry (AI) and Problem-Focused Questions Technique.
- Additional Appreciative Enquiry Questions.
- Understanding the Gratitude/Appreciation Journal Technique.
- The Mobile Gratitude/Appreciation Journal.
- Daily Or Weekly Journal.
- My Appreciation Book.
- Aspirational Gratitude Journal.
- The Calming Techniques.

We have presented a summary of the techniques below and more details are covered in each chapter that follow.

2.1 The Appreciative Enquiry questions.

The Appreciative Enquiry questions help us to explore and identify available, existing, new, or previously successful best possible solutions, strengths and resources to address a current difficult situation.

2.2 The problem-focused questions.

The problem-focused questions tend to dig into and request explanation of what went wrong, what happened or what is happening rather than 'how do we fix' this situation?'.

2.3 The Gratitude/Appreciation Journal Technique.

The Gratitude/Appreciation Journal Technique helps you allow yourself to be thankful for what you have, to appreciate yourself, others, and your environment, to believe and reward yourself, to show compassion and kindness to yourself: to invest in thinking and doing nice things for yourself without neglecting people who need you.

2.4 The Calming Techniques.

The Calming Techniques help to create calmness that improve the quality of sleep, reduce anxiety, and reduce the replaying of unhelpful trauma (emotional injuries) memories.

2.5 Links to Emotions, Physical Reactions, and Happy Hormones.

Collectively, the techniques contribute to positive emotions, physical reactions (joy, contentment, calmness, etc.) and the release of happy hormones (serotonin) in your body. Serotonin produces many emotional and medical benefits that include reducing anxiety by producing calmness, and increasing the strength of your immune system, and slowing aging.

Chapter 3
APPRECIATIVE ENQUIRY AND PROBLEM-FOCUSED QUESTIONS TECHNIQUES

This chapter looks at two slightly opposing tools, one that 'focuses on what's working well' and the other focusing on what is not working well.

3.1 The Appreciative Enquiry questions technique.

The Appreciative Enquiry (AI) technique is summarised by East London Foundation Trust (2021) as an approach *'for creating and sustaining change that focuses on what's working well and seeks to build on this, instead of a more traditional focus on problems and weaknesses. This approach doesn't pretend there are no real or challenging problems, but it asks you to look at them and redefine them in a way that generates several positive possibilities. So instead of starting with 'what's the problem' and looking for fixes it starts with 'what's already working' and how can we build on that?' (retrieved 25 September 2021).*

How true may this be for you now? If yes, what? If no, why?

_____

_____

_____

The Appreciative Enquiry questions focus on helping us to explore and identify available, existing, new, or previously successful

- ▶ Best possible solutions to a difficult situation or a way out or a way forward with a problem.
- ▶ Strengths (example, skills, experiences, etc).
- ▶ Resources (example, money, time, people who may be able to assist, etc.).

3.2 Examples of appreciative questions.

- ▶ *What have you tried before that worked well?*
- ▶ *What do you already know that will or may work well?*
- ▶ *What strengths, skills, and experiences you have that could help?*
- ▶ *How could you /we make things or the situation better?*
- ▶ *What could you /we do to reduce the problem?*
- ▶ *How can you /we assist to improve the situation?*
- ▶ *What was/will be useful?*
- ▶ *What can help to bring positive/desired results?*
- ▶ *Do you know any person who has successfully dealt with a similar situation? What would this person say or recommend as a good plan, strategy, or outcome?*
- ▶ *Do you know any individual who may or can successfully deal with this situation? What would this person say or recommend as a good plan, strategy, or outcome?*

13

How true may this be for you now? If yes, what? If no, why?

_____

_____

_____

3.3 The forebrain response to appreciative questions.

When appreciative questions are asked, the forebrain goes into helpful problem solving and creativity mode. The forebrain invests its resources to help find helpful solutions or a way out or around the problem we are facing. When the brain is in its helpful problem solving and creativity mode, it will trigger the release of the happy or creative hormones (example, serotonin). These hormones help with our body immune system, reduce stress levels, slow down ageing, etc. *For more details on the brain and hormones , see Book One titled 'Do I Have a Twin Brain?' or the Twin Brain web or mobile app at* www.twinbrain.org.

In summary, the appreciate questions may trigger the brain's secondary job of making our lives to be creative, innovative, and happy and less focus on worrying over dangers or threats.

3.4 The problem-focused questions technique.

The problem focused, pathology focused questions or the 'problem saturated questions' techniques are the same. The questions tend to dig into and request explanation of what went wrong, what happened or what is happening rather than 'how do we fix' this situation?'. These types of questions are not bad if the goal is to have a useful understanding of the situation, the problem or the condition being presented or reported by the person being questioned. Both appreciative enquiry and problem focused questions are helpful depending on the reason, the context or the length and resources used up during the questioning.

Example of problem focused question

☐ *Why did you forget your library access card?* Here you want to know and make a note of the reasons given for forgetting

14

the card. How likely is he/she to start by telling you *"I forgot because"*...

How true may this be for you at the now ? If yes, what? If no, why?

_____

_____

_____

3.5 The forebrain's response to problem-focused questions.

One challenge with problem focused questions is that the person's forebrain uses the senses to scan and evaluate you as a threat. If the forebrain concludes that you and your questions are threats, it passes the intelligence information to the amygdala (security department of the brain). The forebrain may base its threat analysis and results on previous unhelpful data on attacks or threats to this person. The amygdala can activate one of its

15

protective modes to try to protect the person from you or get you off the person's back. The protective mode activated may the attack mode (example, irritability/anger to start a fight) or the defensive mode that may be avoidance response, pretence, feeling overwhelmed/helpless, etc. The brain will help the person to find an explanation to protect their survival from you and around you. In the meantime, the original problem remains unresolved because the brain will be investing its resources to protect rather than generating helpful solutions out off or through the difficult situation. When the brain is in protective mode, it will trigger the release of stress or protective hormones (example, adrenaline/cortisones).

How true may this be for you now? If yes, what? If no, why?

_____

_____

_____

For more details on the brain and hormones , see Book One titled 'Do I Have a Twin Brain?' or the Twin Brain web or mobile app at www.twinbrain.org.

In summary, the *why: how:* and *what* or similar questions may trigger the brain's attack or defence mode to deal with a danger or threat. The exception may be if your questions are intended to get details about a good event, situation, or an experience. If the question is about a good situation, the brain is likely to respond as it will to an appreciative enquiry question.

Examples of problem focused questions

- ▶ Why did you do it?
- ▶ What happened?
- ▶ How did it happen?
- ▶ What did you do?

How true may this be for you at the moment ? If yes, what? If no, why?

_____

_____

_____

3.6 What's next?

Now that you have worked through this section, you should pause and reflect on your answers. Put the book aside for a few minutes before answering the questions below

What have you learned and achieved from this section?

_____

_____

_____

What self-help coping technique do you want to learn?

_____

_____

_____

Are there any questions you would like to ask medical professionals?

_____

_____

_____

What specific self-improvement goal or achievement do you want to set for yourself for the next week?

_____

_____

_____

It may be useful to provide yourself with at least five minutes a week to regularly review and reflect on your self-improvement goal. If you do not set aside time to take care of your wellbeing, the daily demands of life may overwhelm you, and it will become harder to develop self-help techniques.

Do not ignore your well-being because life is not endless here on earth. Try to do at least one small act of kindness, compassion, or self-care for yourself today.

My Review Date _____ Time _____ Place _____

3.7 Your Feedback.

The Twin Brain Project Team would like to hear from you if you have helpful suggestions that could help them to improve any aspect of this section for other users. Email your suggestions to admin@twinbrain.org. Please copy info@healthbj-uk.org into your email to make sure your feedback is received. Thank you in advance for helping to improve the Twin Brain resource.

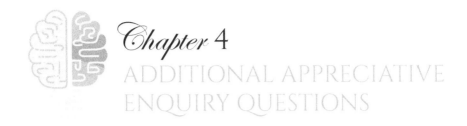

Chapter 4
ADDITIONAL APPRECIATIVE ENQUIRY QUESTIONS

4.1 Appreciative Questions.

What kind of situations make you feel better in your daily life?

Example:
Drinking a cup of natural juice with no sugar or a cup of clean water in the morning.

a)
b)
c)
d)

What does it make you feel?

Example:

Refreshed, hopeful.
a)
b)
c)
d)

What would you say of someone else who had this experience? What does this experience say about you as a person? How do you know this helpful self-label, belief, or voice) to be true or what is the source of your evidence/fact? This is a chance to create a new helpful self-label, belief or voice to challenge any existing unhelpful self-label, belief, or voice.

Example:

I'm doing self-care.

a)
b)
c)
d)

Action Points

Are there any small step action you can take or you need to take to experience this good thing again or to experience a similar or a different good thing?

Example:

To drink fewer cups of natural juice with no sugar and more cups of clean water.

a)
b)
c)
d)

4.2 Appreciative Questions.

In the past or right now, what things or coping techniques made you feel better in your daily life?

Example:

In the past, it was calming and healing to spend 10 minutes in the morning on my silent prayers and mindfulness.

a)
b)
c)
d)

What does it make you feel?

Example:

Serene, protected.

a)
b)
c)
d)

What would you say of someone else who had this experience? What does this experience say about you as a person? How do you know this helpful self-label, belief, or voice to be true or what is the source of your evidence/fact? This is a chance to create a new helpful self-label, belief or voice to challenge any existing unhelpful self-label, belief, or voice.

Example:

I've faith/spirituality to draw strength from and re-charge my depleted wellbeing energy.

a)

b)

c)

d)

Action Points

Are there any small step action you can take to experience this good thing again or to experience a similar or a different good thing?

Example:

To resume spending 10 minutes in the morning on my silent prayers and mindfulness.

a)

b)

c)

d)

4.3 Appreciative Questions.

What 3 things do you still like, enjoy or are passionate about, despite the problems or challenges in your daily life?

Example:

Swimming on weekends and during holidays.

a)

b)

c)

d)

What does it make you feel?

Example:

Tired, but replenished.

a)

b)

c)

d)

What would you say of someone else who had this experience? What does this experience say about you as a person? How do you know this helpful self-label, belief, or voice to be true or what is the source of your evidence/fact? This is a chance to create a new helpful self-label, belief or voice to challenge any existing unhelpful self-label, belief, or voice.

Example:

I love swimming.

a)

b)

c)

d)

Action Points

Are there any small step action you can take to experience this good thing again or to experience a similar or a different good thing?

Example:

To find out and read more about the wellbeing benefits of swimming.

a)

b)

c)

d)

4.4 Appreciative Questions.

What 3 best-case scenarios do you want to achieve in the next 24 hours, or next 3 days or next 7 days?

Example:

Have sound peaceful nine hours' sleep this Saturday morning.

a)

b)

c)

d)

What does it make you feel?

Example:

Rested, energised.

a)

b)

c)

d)

What would you say of someone else who had this experience? What does this experience say about you as a person? How do you know this helpful self-label, belief, or voice) to be true or what is the source of your evidence/fact? This is a chance to create a new helpful self-label, belief or voice to challenge any existing unhelpful self-label, belief, or voice.

Example:

I'm good at self-care for my wellbeing.
a)
b)
c)
d)

Action Points

Are there any small step action you can or need to take to experience this good thing again or to experience a similar or a different good thing?

Example:

Add a self-reminder on my phone to go to bed 9pm (rather than the usual 12am) this Saturday
a)
b)
c)
d)

4.5 Appreciative Questions.

What 3 activities have you stopped doing as routine or you stopped enjoying or you stopped feeling passionate about because of the problems or challenges in your daily life, but you can re-start again?

Example:

Five minutes' early morning run or brisk walk every day to and from my nearest local bus stop.

a)
b)
c)
d)

What does it make you feel?

Example:

Alert, active.
a)
b)
c)
d)

What would you say of someone else who had this experience? What does this experience say about you as a person? How do you know this helpful self-label, belief, or voice) to be true or what is the source of your evidence/fact? This is a chance to create a new helpful self-label, belief or voice to challenge any existing unhelpful self-label, belief, or voice.

Example:

I look after my physical and mental health.

a)

b)

c)

d)

Action Points

Are there any small step action you can or you need to take to experience this good thing again or to experience a similar or a different good thing?

Example

Keep doing my early morning run and brisk walk.

a)

b)

c)

d)

4.6 Appreciative Questions.

What 3 good things have you stopped dreaming of, because of the problems or challenges in your daily life, but you can re-start dreaming again?

Example:

To go on holiday to a sea beach.

a)

b)

c)

d)

What does it make you feel?

Example:

Welcoming, spontaneous.

a)

b)

c)

d)

What would you say of someone else who had this experience? What does this experience say about you as a person? How do you know this helpful self-label, belief, or voice) to be true or what is the source of your evidence/fact? This is a chance to create a new helpful self-label, belief or voice to challenge any existing unhelpful self-label, belief, or voice.

Example:

I'm capable of re-igniting lost dreams.

a)
b)
c)
d)

Action Points

Are there any small step action you can or need to take to experience this good thing again or to experience a similar or a different good thing?

Example:

Save money, find, and visit the seaside of my dream.

a)
b)
c)
d)

4.7 Appreciative Questions.

Who are the 3 positive people you surround yourself with?
Example:

Master Samuel Tamaranamene, my three years' old son who keeps inspiring me, as well as challenging my gaps in many areas of life with his four language skills (Ijon/Ijaw, Russian, English, Ukrainian) and exploring engineering talents.

a)
b)
c)
d)

What does it make you feel?
Example:

Challenged, inspired.

a)
b)
c)
d)

What would you say of someone else who had this experience? What does this experience say about you as a person? How do you know this helpful self-label, belief, or voice) to be true or what is the source of your evidence/fact? This is a chance to create a new helpful self-label, belief or voice to challenge any existing unhelpful self-label, belief, or voice.

Example:

I'm open minded and willing to learning.

a)
b)
c)

Action Points

Are there any small step you can or need to take to experience this good thing again or to experience a similar or a different good thing?

Example:

To ask for and be ready for touch and sweet feedback from family members, friends, work peers and managers.

a)

b)

c)

d)

4.8 Appreciative Questions.

Who are the 3 people who inspire you?
Example:

Nelson Mandela.

a)

b)

c)

d)

What does it make you feel?
Example:

Heroic, humble.

a)

b)

c)

d)

What would you say of someone else who had this experience? What does this experience say about you as a person? How do you know this helpful self-label, belief, or voice to be true or what is the source of your evidence/fact? This is a chance to create a new helpful self-label, belief or voice to challenge any existing unhelpful self-label, belief, or voice.

Example:

I can be my hero and a hero for someone.

a)

b)

c)

d)

Action Points

Are there any small step action I can or I need to do to re-experience this good thing again or to experience a similar or a different good thing?

Example:

To do at least one random act of heroic kindness for myself or someone in a month.
a)
b)
c)
d)

4.9 Appreciative Questions.

How much do you value yourself? What money price tag would you place on yourself? How important do you consider yourself to be right now? Rate 0 (no appreciation) to 100 (highest or best).

Example:

Score *e.g., 45 out of 100.*

If you are seeing yourself below 50 value, then from today, you can raise your value to 60 percent or more and start to take small step actions to make it a reality in the future.

a)
b)
c)
d)

What does it make you feel?

Example:

Not good enough.
a)
b)
c)
d)

What would you say of someone else who had this experience? What does this experience say about you as a person? How do you know this helpful self-label, belief, or voice) to be true or what is the source of your evidence/fact? This is a chance to create a new helpful self-label, belief or voice to challenge any existing unhelpful self-label, belief, or voice.

Example:

If I see less value in me or under-sell my self-worth, why should other people treat me different?
a)
b)
c)
d)

Action Points

Are there any small step action you can or need to take to experience this good thing again or to experience a similar or a different good thing?

Example:

To make a list of all my assets-skills, training, experiences etc and everything I'm good at.

a)
b)
c)
d)

4.10 Appreciative Questions.

The 3 good things, values, or standards I stand for and believe in. What kind of good person do I want to be in my personal life?

Example:

Talking myself and other people up and not to talk down.

a)
b)
c)
d)

What does it make you feel?

Example:

Inspiring, building up.

a)
b)
c)
d)

What would you say of someone else who had this experience? What does this experience say about you as a person? How do you know this helpful self-label, belief, or voice to be true or what is the source of your evidence/fact? This is a chance to create a new helpful self-label, belief or voice to challenge any existing unhelpful self-label, belief, or voice.

Example:

I'm an inspirer, enabler, encourager.

a)
b)
c)
d)

Action Points

Are there any small step action I can or I need to do to re-experience this good thing again or to experience a similar or a different good thing?

28

Example:

Tell myself or someone one positively unique quality at least a fortnight.
a)
b)
c)
d)

4.11 Appreciative Questions.

The 3 good things, values, or standards I stand for and believe in. What kind of good person I want to be in my public life?

Example:

Honesty
a)
b)
c)
d)

What does it make you feel?
Example:

Clear conscience, dependable.
a)
b)
c)
d)

What would you say of someone else who had this experience? What does this experience say about you as a person? How do you know this helpful self-label, belief, or voice) to be true or what is the source of your evidence/fact? This is a chance to create a new helpful self-label, belief or voice to challenge any existing unhelpful self-label, belief, or voice.

Example:

I'm trustworthy.
a)
b)
c)
d)

Action Points

Are there any small step action I can or I need to do to re-experience this good thing again or to experience a similar or a different good thing?

Example:

Tell my work colleagues the truth that I thank them and I like to accept their invite to this weekend's social party, but I can't on this occasion because it's my daughter's graduation ceremony.

a)
b)
c)
d)

4.12 Appreciative Questions.

3 good things, values, or standards you believe in. What kind of good person do want to be at work?

Example:

Helpful team player.

a)
b)
c)
d)

What does it make you feel?
Example:

Close, involved.

a)
b)
c)
d)

What would you say of some else who had this experience? What does this experience say about you as a person? How do you know this helpful self-label, belief, or voice to be true or what is the source of your evidence/fact? This is a chance to create a new helpful self-label, belief or voice to challenge any existing unhelpful self-label, belief, or voice.

Example:

I see people's needs and preferences and I'm able to assist them while not ignoring my own needs and preferences.

a)
b)
c)
d)

Action Points

Are there any small step action you can or need to do to experience this good thing again or to experience a similar or a different good thing?

Example:

Do one random act of kindness for a team member or for the whole team at least once a month.

a)
b)
c)
d)

4.13 What's next?

Now that you have worked through this section, you should pause and reflect on your answers. Put the book aside for a few minutes before answering the questions below

☐ What have you learned and achieved from this section?

_____

_____

_____

☐ What self-help coping techniques do you want to learn?

_____

_____

_____

☐ Are there any questions you would like to ask medical professionals?

_____

_____

_____

☐ What specific self-improvement goal or achievement do you want to set for yourself for the next week?

_____

_____

_____

It may be useful to provide yourself with at least five minutes a week to regularly review and reflect on your self-improvement goal. If you do not set aside time to take care of your wellbeing, the daily demands of life may overwhelm you, and it will become harder to develop self-help techniques.

Do not ignore your well-being because life is not endless here on earth. Try to do at least one small act of kindness, compassion, or self-care for yourself today.

My Review Date _____ Time _____ Place _____

4.14 Your Feedback.

The Twin Brain Project Team would like to hear from you if you have helpful suggestions that could help them to improve any aspect of this section for other users. Email your suggestions to admin@twinbrain.org. Please copy info@healthbj-uk.org into your email to make sure your feedback is received. Thank you in advance for helping to improve the Twin Brain resource.

Chapter 5
UNDERSTANDING THE GRATITUDE/APPRECIATION JOURNAL TECHNIQUE

In this chapter we are going to explain Gratitude Journaling. This is the process of writing down what you are grateful for, or what you appreciate.

5.1 What does gratitude or appreciation mean to me'?

First we must ask ourselves – 'What does gratitude or appreciation mean to me'?

_____

_____

_____

Examples,

- Being thankful for what I have. Appreciating myself, others, and my environment. Believing in myself and rewarding myself.
- Showing compassion and kindness to myself. Investing in, thinking of, and doing nice things for myself without neglecting people who need me.
- Asking who am I? What are my goals?

How true are the above examples for you at the moment? If yes, why? If no, why?

5.2 Do you do positive and negative journaling?

The keeping of a diary of the bad things that happened to you is a form of negative journaling. It is not a right or wrong thing to create a negative journal, but be sure the reason is a helpful one. Example, a negative journal in a war situation or in an abusive relationship shall assist other people to become aware of, learn from and give needed support now or in the future. However, getting stuck in and living our lives in the past negative experiences could reduce our chances of creating a happier or a more resilience future for ourselves and for other people. Negative journaling may create negative emotions, bodily reactions, and stress (cortisone) hormones

How true is this for you now? If yes, why? If no, why?

5.3 What can a positive gratitude journal do for you?

▶ The positive emotions and bodily reactions (such as joy, contentment, calmness) you feel during the period of showing yourself gratitude may be linked to happy hormones (serotonin) being released into your body. Serotonin produces many emotional and medical benefits that include reducing anxiety by making you feel relaxed, improving your immune system (ability to recover from illness) and slows down aging.

▶ It helps you understand what is important, and what you can control. For example, it is not necessary to worry about something that is very unlikely to happen.

▶ It makes you think about how much of your time you spend focusing on gratitude or appreciation of things good versus unhelpful things.

▶ A gratitude journal may help to activate good old memories. You can look at them when you are older and remember old memories. You may even choose to pass them to your children and grandchildren.

▶ It is a source to challenge unhelpful thoughts.

▶ Positive emotions, bodily reactions and hormones may contribute to feelings of positivity, innovation, creativity, and good mental health.

- It may help to develop or increase motivation/desire in yourself to do and achieve things and to believe in yourself. Feeling happy or proud over things you have achieved or things you are good at, can remind your brain that you have the ability to do well and take positive steps to improve your life.

5.4 Types of gratitude journals.

You can make your journal anyway you like! Although most people do it in writing, you can use pictures, sounds, videos or anything else that you like to use.

- **Written Journal** You can write notes about good things that happen to you. It can be on paper, post-it notes you stick on your fridge or at your desk. It can be text message to yourself. You can write a Word document and save it on your computer.
- **Photo Journal** You can take photographs or keep photos about good things that happen to you and around you. Lots of people do this without realizing it – if you have photos of friends, family and loved ones in your home you are already doing this!
- **Audio Journal** You can record good things that happened to you and around you. Your mobile phone may be useful for quick recording and playing back to listen.

- ▶ **Video Journal** You can make a video record of good things that happened to you and around you. Again, your mobile phone is good for this.
- ▶ **Picture Journal** You can draw, paint, colour in or use any form of art to remind yourself of the good things that have happened to you. For example, you, might keep a flower (or a photo of the flower) as a reminder of a happy moment in your life.

How true are the above examples for you at the moment? If yes, why? If no, why?

_____

_____

_____

Or which type of journal above do you feel is more comfortable for you?

_____

_____

_____

5.5 How to Complete Your Gratitude Journal?

You should work on your journal at your own pace. You can put it down and return to it whenever you want.

If you decide to use the Twin Brain App to journal your good memories, a copy will be saved in your account for 3 months from the date you start your Journal (after 3 months it will be automatically deleted). If you're worried about losing it, you should email a copy to yourself because it can never be replaced.

Are You Ready to Step Into The World of Appreciation?

(a)Am I able to appreciate myself and feel appreciated without being a self-love (narcissistic) arrogant? If yes, why? If not, why not?

_____

_____

_____

(b) Am I able to appreciate anyone or other people? If yes, why? If not, why not?

_____

_____

_____

5.6 Example of Journals.

It can be hard to simply sit down and start writing, talking, or drawing about your feelings, so we have created some ideas of how to structure your journal below. You can edit and change the examples below as much as you like – it's your journal!

- ▶ The Mobile Gratitude/Appreciation Journal.
- ▶ The Daily or Weekly Gratitude Journal.
- ▶ My Appreciation Book.
- ▶ Aspirational Gratitude Journal.

5.7 What's next?

Now that you have worked through this section, you should pause and reflect on your answers. Put the book aside for a few minutes before answering the questions below

☐ What have you learned and achieved from this section?

_____

_____

_____

☐ What self-help coping techniques do you want to learn?

_____

_____

_____

_____

_____

_____

☐ Are there any questions you would like to ask medical professionals?

_____

_____

_____

☐ What specific self-improvement goal or achievement do you want to set for yourself for the next week?

_____

_____

_____

It may be useful to provide yourself with at least five minutes a week to regularly review and reflect on your self-improvement goal. If you do not set aside time to take care of your wellbeing, the daily demands of life may overwhelm you, and it will become harder to develop self-help techniques.

Do not ignore your well-being because life is not endless here on earth. Try to do at least one small act of kindness, compassion, or self-care for yourself today.

My Review Date _____ **Time** _____ Place _____

5.8 Your Feedback.

The Twin Brain Project Team would like to hear from you if you have helpful suggestions that could help them to improve any aspect of this section for other users. Email your suggestions to admin@twinbrain.org. Please copy info@healthbj-uk.org into your email to make sure your feedback is received. Thank you in advance for helping to improve the Twin Brain resource.

Chapter 6
THE MOBILE GRATITUDE/ APPRECIATION JOURNAL

The Mobile Journal is created on the spot and as you go about your day's tasks. The table below shows an example.

6.1 Example of a Mobile Journal.

What was or is it?
Make a quick note now or on the spot of a good thing that has happened to you.

The good, beautiful, amazing, unique, wonderful, happy, or proud situation, event, experience, skills, or achievements that I appreciate or I am thankful for?

Example:
'Relationship with my partner - We communicate well. Naturally good. Good team'.

Example:
'A nice run'.
a)
b)
c)

What did or does it make you feel?

On the spot or later, ask yourself how the good thing you have identified is making you to feel when you recall the good thing.

Example:

'It made me happy'.
a)
b)
c)
d)

Example:

'Nice feeling'.
a)
b)
c)
d)

What would you say of someone else who had this experience? What does this experience say about you as a person? How do you know this helpful self-label, belief, or voice to be true or what is the source of your evidence/fact? This is a chance to create a new helpful self-label, belief or voice to challenge any existing unhelpful self-label, belief, or voice.

Example:

'Maybe I'm a good person. Maybe I'm not worthless. I can't be a terrible person if I'm attracting love'. These are new labels.
a)
b)
c)
d)

Example:

'I'm the person who gains satisfaction and peace'.
a)
b)
c)
d)

Action Points.

Are there any small step action you can or need to take to experience this good thing again or to experience a similar or a different good thing?

Example:

'To explore and reflect more on the new labels. To write a poem'.
a)
b)
c)
d)

Example:

'To tap into the new label above more'.

a)

b)

c)

d)

6.2 What's next?

Now that you have worked through this section, you should pause and reflect on your answers. Put the book aside for a few minutes before answering the questions below

☐ What have you learned and achieved from this section?

_____

_____

_____

☐ What self-help coping techniques do you want to learn?

_____

_____

_____

☐ Are there any questions you would like to ask medical professionals?

_____

_____

_____

☐ What specific self-improvement goal or achievement do you want to set for yourself for the next week?

_____

_____

_____

It may be useful to provide yourself with at least five minutes a week to regularly review and reflect on your self-improvement goal. If you do not set aside time to take care of your wellbeing, the daily demands of life may overwhelm you, and it will become harder to develop self-help techniques.

Do not ignore your well-being because life is not endless here on earth. Try to do at least one small act of kindness, compassion, or self-care for yourself today.

My Review Date ——————— **Time** ————— Place —————————

6.3 Your Feedback.

The Twin Brain Project Team would like to hear from you if you have helpful suggestions that could help them to improve any aspect of this section for other users. Email your suggestions to admin@twinbrain.org. Please copy info@healthbj-uk.org into your email to make sure your feedback is received. Thank you in advance for helping to improve the Twin Brain resource.

Chapter 7
THE DAILY OR WEEKLY GRATITUDE JOURNAL

The Daily or Weekly Journal is created at the end of the day or once a week depending on how much time you have to invest on working on your journal. Below is an example.

7.1 The Daily Or Weekly Journal Section A.

What 3 things or behaviours went well for you this week?
Example:

a) My line manager told me my project report was excellent.

b) Had a great swimming with a friend.

c) Went over to say 'hello and welcome' to my new neighbours after 6 weeks of putting it off when they moved to our street.

d)

e)

f)

How did or does it make you feel?

Example:

a) Relieved. Proud of myself and my team.

b) Refreshed. Full of energy.

c) Burden of guilt lifted. Connected to my new neighbours.

d)

e)

f)

What would you say of someone else who had this experience? What does this experience say about you as a person? How do you know this helpful self-label, belief, or voice to be true or what is the source of your evidence/fact? *This is a chance to create a new helpful self-label, belief or voice to challenge any existing unhelpful self-label, belief, or voice.*

Example:

a) A reminder that I'm very skilled at what I do. I'm a talent.

b) I can do self-care if I take a little step to overcome my initial hesitation.

c) I'm capable of reaching out to and connecting with people. I make people feel welcome and accepted.

d)

e)

f)

Action Points.

Are there any small step action you can or need to take to experience this good thing again or to experience a similar or a different good thing?

Example:

a) To chat and explore with my line manager what I need to do to move to the next level of my career within the next 24 months.

b) To swim by myself or with a friend twice a month.

c) To phone or message one family member or one old friend last Saturday of each month.

d)

e)

f)

7.2 The Daily or Weekly Journal Section B.

What 3 things or behaviours did not go well for you this week?

Example:

a) I forgot to say sorry to my aunt when I sent her birthday card after her birthday celebration this week.

b) I was 30 minutes late to work due to traffic.

c) I missed all my mindfulness practices/prayers.

d)

e)

f)

What 3 positive things can you learn from these 3 things or behaviours?

Example:

a) My job is taking over my existence and I need to find some time to look after my self-care.

b) I need to improve my time management.

c) I need to look into what is really important for my wellbeing and happiness while not ignoring my job.

d)

e)

f)

What small step actions have you taken, or could take to resolve each of the 3 things or behaviours that did not go well for me this week? Is there anything you could have done differently that would be more helpful?

Example:

a) Put important events on my diary with 2 weeks advance notifications.

b) Find alternative routes with least traffic jam or add 45 minutes to my usual time of leaving home.

c) Make my mindfulness practices/prayers time as 'protected and not to be missed activities' on my diary with one hour advance notifications.

d)

e)

f)

NOTE *If you require techniques to assist you to translate your identified small step actions into reality, then see the Behaviour Change Experiment in this book or in the Twin Brain App and website.*

7.3 What's next?

Now that you have worked through this section, you should pause and reflect on your answers. Put the book aside for a few minutes before answering the questions below

☐ What have you learned and achieved from this section?

_____

_____

_____

☐ What self-help coping techniques do you want to learn?

_____

_____

_____

☐ Are there any questions you would like to ask medical professionals?

_____

_____

_____

☐ What specific self-improvement goal or achievement do you want to set for yourself for the next week?

_____

_____

_____

It may be useful to provide yourself with at least five minutes a week to regularly review and reflect on your self-improvement goal. If you do not set aside time to take care of your wellbeing, the daily demands of life may overwhelm you, and it will become harder to develop self-help techniques.

Do not ignore your well-being because life is not endless here on earth. Try to do at least one small act of kindness, compassion, or self-care for yourself today.

47

My Review Date _____ Time _____ Place _____

7.4 Your Feedback.

The Twin Brain Project Team would like to hear from you if you have helpful suggestions that could help them to improve any aspect of this section for other users. Email your suggestions to admin@twinbrain.org. Please copy info@healthbj-uk.org into your email to make sure your feedback is received. Thank you in advance for helping to improve the Twin Brain resource.

Chapter 8
MY APPRECIATION BOOK

In the below example, we separate things into different categories, such as things you are grateful for in your personal life, work life, or anywhere else. You can add or remove categories depending on your own lifestyle.

8.1 My personal Life.

What was it?

The good, beautiful, amazing, unique, wonderful, happy, or proud situation, event, experience, skill, or achievement that you appreciate or are thankful for in your personal life?

Example:

a) I bought a cute kitten. She's fun and plays hide and seek with me.

b) I've an incredible memory for remembering details about most things.

c) I've pretty long hairs.

Write here

a)

b)

c)

What did or does it make you feel?

Ask yourself how the good thing you have identified makes you feel when you recall the good thing.

Example:

a) Relaxed, funny, happy.

b) Proud.

c) Cheerful.

Write here

a)

b)

c)

What would you say of someone else who had this experience? What does this experience say about you as a person? How do you know this helpful self-label, belief, or voice to be true or what is the source of your evidence/fact? *This is a chance to create a new helpful self-label, belief or voice to challenge any existing unhelpful self-label, belief, or voice.*

Example:

a) I can love animals. I've a funny side to me.

b) I'm smart. I'm gifted.

c) I'm beautiful inside and outside.

Write here

a)

b)

c)

Action Point.

Are there any small step action you can or need to take to experience this good thing again or to experience a similar or a different good thing?

Example:

a) To volunteer few hours a weekend for a local animal charity.

b) Check out what extra things I can do with my brilliant memory, including extra cash.

c) To donate hair to help raise fund for an orphanage in Africa or middle east.

Write here

a)

b)

c)

8.2 My work life.

What was it?

The good, beautiful, amazing, unique, wonderful, happy, or proud situation, event, experience, skill, or achievement that you appreciate, or are am thankful for in your work life?

Example:

a) A customer for my firm told me I'm one of the best caring professionals he ever received support from.

b) Got promoted.

c) Organised the team's picnic and it was a wonderful event.

Write here

a)

b)

c)

What did or does it make you feel?

Ask yourself how the good thing you have identified makes you feel when you recall the good thing.

Example:

a) Humbled, delighted, being appreciated.

b) Deserved. Pleased.

c) Fulfilled. Achieved.

Write here

a)

b)

c)

What would you say of someone else who had this experience? What does this experience say about you as a person? How do you know this helpful self-label, belief, or voice to be true or what is the source of your evidence/fact? *This is a chance to create a new helpful self-label, belief or voice to challenge any existing unhelpful self-label, belief, or voice.*

Example:

a) I understand people's needs. I'm a caring person.

b) I can achieve my dreams.

c) I'm a people's person. I'm an encourager.

Write here

a)

b)

c)

Action Point.
Are there any small step action you can or need to do to re-experience this good thing again or to experience a similar or a different good thing?

Example:

a) Keep being authentic in caring for people.

b) Set target for my next career level.

c) To organise a weekend picnic or barbeque for my family and parents.

Write here

a)

b)

c)

8.3 My educational achievements/qualifications.

What was it?
The good, beautiful, amazing, unique, wonderful, happy, or proud situation, event, experience, skill, or achievement that you appreciate, or you are thankful for in relation to your educational achievements/ qualifications?

Example:

a)Cheer Leader.

b)Diploma in fishery.

c) Best student in fishery award.

Write here

a)

b)

c)

What did or does it make you feel?
Ask yourself how the good thing you have identified makes you feel when you recall the good thing.

Example:

Thrilled, pride, daring.

Write here

a)

b)

c)

What would you say of someone else who had this experience? What does this experience say about you as a person? How do you know this helpful self-label, belief, or voice to be true or what is the source of your evidence/fact? *This is a chance to create a new helpful self-label, belief or voice to challenge any existing unhelpful self-label, belief, or voice.*

Example:

a) I've leadership in me.

b) Achiever.

Write here

a)

b)

c)

Action Point.

Are there any small step action you can or need to take to experience this good thing again or to experience a similar or a different good thing?

Example:

Stop being a follower of bad friends who give wrong advice to use drugs to reduce stress. To lead them with good advice to find safer ways of managing life stressors.

Write here

a)

b)

c)

8.4 Other skills, experiences and achievements not included above.

What was it?

The good, beautiful, amazing, unique, wonderful, happy, or proud situation, event, experience, skill, or achievement that you appreciate, or are am thankful for in relation to your other skills, experiences and achievements not included above?

Example:

a) I wrote poems and people loved them.

b) I sing at my Church's choir and my town's music band.

c) I'm a first aider and have helped to save a person who fell on the street.

Write here

a)

b)

c)

What did or does it make you feel?

Ask yourself how the good thing you have identified makes you feel when you recall the good thing.

Example:

Satisfised, enjoy, sympathy, heroic.

Write here

a)

b)

c)

What would you say of someone else who had this experience? What does this experience say about you as a person? How do you know this helpful self-label, belief, or voice to be true or what is the source of your evidence/fact? *This is a chance to create a new helpful self-label, belief or voice to challenge any existing unhelpful self-label, belief, or voice.*

Example:

a)I'm creative and talented.

b)I'm heroic. I'm a helpful person.

Write here

a)

b)

c)

Action Point.

Are there any small step action you need to take to experience this good thing again or to experience a similar or a different good thing?

Example:

a)Put together all my poems over the years and publish them as a book of poems.

b)Keep singing songs.

c)To volunteer as a first aider in my church and in my dance club.

Write here

a)

b)

8.5 Your family (parents) if any)?

**What is good, beautiful, amazing, unique, or wonderful about
Your family (parents) if any)?**

Example:

a)Mum and dad are hard working.

b)My sisters, brothers and our parents are funny and loving.

c)We leave no one behind in any difficult or happy situation we found ourselves.

Write here

a)

b)

c)

What did or does it make you feel?

Ask yourself how the good thing you have identified makes you feel when you recall the good thing.

Example:

Laughter, unselfish, warm

Write here

a)

b)

c)

What would you say of someone else who had this experience? What does this experience say about you as a person? How do you know this helpful self-label, belief, or voice to be true or what is the source of your evidence/fact? *This is a chance to create a new helpful self-label, belief or voice to challenge any existing unhelpful self-label, belief, or voice.*

Example:

a)I'm part of a gracious family.

b)I'm a family person.

c)I'm capable of creating a fun loving and hardworking family of my own someday.

Write here

a)

b)

c)

Action Point.

Are there any small step action you can or need to take to experience this good thing again or to experience a similar or a different good thing?

Example:

a)To share my family values with other people.

b)To tell my siblings and my parents how I'm lucky to have them in my life.

c)To make a list of the values I want in my life partner.

Write here

a)

b)

c)

8.6 Your family (children) if any).

What is good, beautiful, amazing, unique, or wonderful about Your family (children) if any)?

Example:

a)A gorgeous niece.

b)A cute nephew.

Write here

a)

b)

c)

What did or does it make you feel?

Ask yourself how the good thing you have identified makes you feel when you recall the good thing.

Example:

Lucky, affection, wonder, tender.

Write here

a)

b)

c)

What would you say of someone else who had this experience? What does this experience say about you as a person? How do you know this helpful self-label, belief, or voice to be true or what is the source of your evidence/fact? *This is a chance to create a new helpful self-label, belief or voice to challenge any existing unhelpful self-label, belief, or voice.*

Example:

a) I'm a children lover.

b) I shall be a wonderful parent.

Write here

a)

b)

c)

Action Point.

Are there any small step action you can or need to take to experience this good thing again or to experience a similar or a different good thing?

Example:

▶ *Spend more time to see and play with my niece and nephew.*

▶ *To baby sit more and give some space for my married siblings with kids to go out for fun.*

Write here

a)

b)

c)

8.7 Your other family members (if any).

What is good, beautiful, amazing, unique, or wonderful about Your other family members (if any)?

Example:

▶ *A great story telly aunt.*

▶ *A generous uncle.*

▶ *Granddad with excellent carpentry skills.*

Write here

a)

b)

c)

What did or does it make you feel?

Ask yourself how the good thing you have identified makes you feel when you recall the good thing.

Example:

Appreciate, secured, admire, compassion.

Write here

a)

b)

c)

What would you say of some else who had this experience? What does this experience say about you as a person? How do you know this helpful self-label, belief, or voice to be true or what is the source of your evidence/fact? *This is a chance to create a new helpful self-label, belief or voice to challenge any existing unhelpful self-label, belief, or voice.*

Example:

▶ *I'm well connected and able to connect.*

▶ *I'm a social person and can reach out to people in need.*

Write here

a)

b)

c)

Action Point.

Are there any small step action you can or need to take to experience this good thing again or to experience a similar or a different good thing?

Example:

▶ *Tell my aunts, uncles, and grandparents that I appreciate them.*

▶ *Start to audio and video record family stories and granddad's carpentry works for future generations.*

Write here

a)

b)

c)

8.8 Your wife/husband/romantic partner (if any).

What is good, beautiful, amazing, unique, or wonderful about your wife/husband/ romantic partner (if any)?

Example:

▶ *A loyal fiancée.*

▶ *Loves children.*

Write here

a)

b)

c)

What did or does it make you feel?
Ask yourself how the good thing you have identified makes you feel when you recall the good thing.

Example:

Genuine, close, affection.

Write here

a)

b)

c)

What would you say of someone else who had this experience? What does this experience say about you as a person? How do you know this helpful self-label, belief, or voice to be true or what is the source of your evidence/fact? *This is a chance to create a new helpful self-label, belief or voice to challenge any existing unhelpful self-label, belief, or voice.*

Example:

▶ *I know what values I want in a life partner.*

▶ *I can make a relationship work for me and the other person.*

Write here

a)

b)

c)

Action Point.
Are there any small step action you can or need to take to experience this good thing again or to experience a similar or a different good thing?

Example:

▶ *To talk how I feel honestly, but with respect to my partner.*

▶ *Never insult, be rude or put down my partner even if I disagree with what is said to me.*

Write here

a)

b)

c)

8.9 Your friends/social network.

What is good, beautiful, amazing, unique, or wonderful about Your friends/social network?

Example:

Volunteer to teach wellbeing skills and play football with children in my community.

Write here

a)

b)

c)

What did or does it make you feel?
Ask yourself how the good thing you have identified makes you feel when you recall the good thing.

Example:

Fulfilled, connected.

Write here

a)

b)

c)

What would you say of some else who had this experience? What does this experience say about you as a person? How do you know this helpful self-label, belief, or voice to be true or what is the source of your evidence/fact? *This is a chance to create a new helpful self-label, belief or voice to challenge any existing unhelpful self-label, belief, or voice.*

Example:

▶ *I'm capable of sharing my talents and enjoy fun.*

Write here

a)

b)

c)

Action Point.
Are there any small step action you can or need to take to experience this good thing again or to experience a similar or a different good thing?

Example:

▶ *To teach kids-to- kids mental wellbeing skills.*

Write here

a)

b)

c)

8.10 Things/qualities people appreciate about You.

What things or qualities do people appreciate about you ?

Example:

▶ *My nephew said I'm the sweetest darling uncle in the universe.*

Write here

a)

b)

c)

What did or does it make you feel?
Ask yourself how the good thing you have identified makes you feel when you recall the good thing.

Example:

▶ *Proud and glad.*

Write here

a)

b)

c)

What would you say of someone else who had this experience? What does this experience say about you as a person? How do you know this helpful self-label, belief, or voice to be true or what is the source of your evidence/fact? *This is a chance to create a new helpful self-label, belief or voice to challenge any existing unhelpful self-label, belief, or voice.*

Example:

▶ *I'm a lovely and caring person.*
▶ *How do I know this? My nephew confirmed it.*

Write here

a)

b)

c)

Action Point.
Are there any small step action you can or need to take to experience this good thing again or to experience a similar or a different good thing?

Example:

Create a certificate with the words *'I'm the sweetest darling uncle in the universe. I'm a lovely and caring person. I'm proud and glad'.*

Write here
a)
b)
c)

8.11 Nature in relation to plants/trees.

What is good, beautiful, amazing, unique, or wonderful about nature in relation to plants/trees?

Example:

I spent time by the pond in my local Park and I watched the fish swimming and feeding from the leftover breadcrumbs.

Write here
a)
b)
c)

What did or does it make me feel?
Ask yourself how the good thing you have identified makes you feel when you recall the good thing.

Example:

Refreshing and lost at the wonders of nature.

Write here
a)
b)
c)

What would you say of some else who had this experience? What does this experience say about you as a person? How do you know this helpful self-label, belief, or voice to be true or what is the source of your evidence/fact? *This is a chance to create a new helpful self-label, belief or voice to challenge any existing unhelpful self-label, belief, or voice.*

Example:

I should appreciate nature and not to see my current hectic work life as the epic of my existence on earth.

Write here
a)
b)
c)

Action Point.
Are there any small step action you can or need to do to experience this good thing again or to experience a similar or a different good thing?

Example:
My next nature's exploration shall be a visit to my local deer Park.

Write here
a)
b)
c)

8.12 Nature in relation to animals.

What is good, beautiful, amazing, unique, or wonderful about nature in relation to Animals?

Example:

My friend's cute puppy sleeps over in my home every weekend during my friend's weekend work shift.

Write here
a)
b)
c)

What did or does it make you feel?
Ask yourself how the good thing you have identified makes you feel when you recall the good thing.

Example:
Playful, laughter.

Write here
a)
b)
c)

What would you say of some else who had this experience? What does this experience say about you as a person? How do you know this helpful self-label, belief, or voice to be true or what is the source of your evidence/fact? *This is a chance to create a new helpful self-label, belief or voice to challenge any existing unhelpful self-label, belief, or voice.*

Example:
I have a playful child nature in me.

Write here
a)
b)
c)

Action Point.
Are there any small step action you can or need to do to experience this good thing again or to experience a similar or a different good thing?

Example:
Get my own puppy next birthday.

Write here
a)
b)
c)

8.13 Nature in relation to climate.

What is good, beautiful, amazing, unique, or wonderful about nature in relation to climate?

Example:
I watch the sunrise and sunset during summer.

Write here
a)
b)
c)

What did or does it make you feel?
Ask yourself how the good thing you have identified makes you feel when you recall the good thing.

Example:
Miraculous, floating on clouds.

Write here
a)
b)
c)

What would you say of some else who had this experience? What does this experience say about you as a person? How do you know this helpful self-label, belief, or voice to be true or what is the source of you evidence/fact? *This is a chance to create a new helpful self-label, belief or voice to challenge any existing unhelpful self-label, belief, or voice.*

Connected to nature and creation.

Write here
a)
b)
c)

Action Point.
Are there any small step action you can or need to experience this good thing again or to experience a similar or a different good thing?

Example:
Keep watching sunrise and sunset during summer.

Write here
a)
b)
c)

8.14 Other aspects of nature that you experience or interact with.

What is good, beautiful, amazing, unique, or wonderful about other aspects of nature that you experience or interact with?

Example:
Watching the aerial video maps of the earth and the galaxies of the universe.

Write here
a)
b)
c)

What did or does it make you feel?
Ask yourself how the good thing you have identified makes you feel when you recall the good thing.

Example:
Mesmerized, blown away, motivated.

Write here
a)
b)
c)

What would you say of some else who had this experience? What does this experience say about you as a person? How do you know this helpful self-label, belief, or voice to be true or what is the source of your evidence/fact? *This is a chance to create a new helpful self-label, belief or voice to challenge any existing unhelpful self-label, belief, or voice.*

Example:

I'm lucky to be born and my existence in the universe is worth celebrating.

Write here
  a)
  b)
  c)

Action Point.

Are there any small step action you can or need to take to experience this good thing again or to experience a similar or a different good thing?

Example:

Buy a powerful telescope to enable me to watch the stars at night.

Write here

a)

b)

c)

8.14 What's next?

Now that you have worked through this section, you should pause and reflect on your answers. Put the book aside for a few minutes before answering the questions below

☐ What have you learned and achieved from this section?

_____

_____

_____

☐ What self-help coping techniques do you want to learn?

_____

_____

_____

☐ Are there any questions you would like to ask medical professionals?

_____

_____

_____

☐ What specific self-improvement goal or achievement do you want to set for yourself for the next week?

_____

_____

_____

It may be useful to provide yourself with at least five minutes a week to regularly review and reflect on your self-improvement goal. If you do not set aside time to take care of your wellbeing, the daily demands of life may overwhelm you, and it will become harder to develop self-help techniques.

Do not ignore your well-being because life is not endless here on earth. Try to do at least one small act of kindness, compassion, or self-care for yourself today.

My Review Date _____ **Time** _____ **Place** _____

8.15 Your Feedback.

The Twin Brain Project Team would like to hear from you if you have helpful suggestions that could help them to improve any aspect of this section for other users. Email your suggestions to admin@twinbrain.org. Please copy info@healthbj-uk.org into your email to make sure your feedback is received. Thank you in advance for helping to improve the Twin Brain resource.

Chapter 9
ASPIRATIONAL GRATITUDE JOURNAL

This chapter gives an opportunity to you to dream and aspire for the good, beautiful, amazing, unique, or wonderful things you want to achieve in the future?

9.1 Your personal life skills, experiences, and achievements.

What is the good, beautiful, amazing, unique, or wonderful thing you want to achieve in the future in relation to your personal life skills, experiences, and achievements?

Example:

To pass and obtain my driving licence.

Write here

a)

b)

c)

How does this goal make you feel? Or, if it becomes a reality for you , how would you feel?

Example:
Excitement, accomplishment.

Write here

a)

b)

c)

What would you say of someone else who had this experience? What would this experience say about you as a person if it becomes a reality? How do you know this helpful self-label, belief, or voice to be true or what is the source of your evidence/ fact? *This is a chance to create a new helpful self-label, belief or voice to challenge any existing unhelpful self-label, belief, or voice.*

Example:
I can achieve my dreams when I'm determined and put efforts.

Write here

a)

b)

c)

Action Points.
Is there any small step action you can or need to take to experience this good thing again or to experience a similar or a different good thing?

Example:
Save enough money to buy the study resource for the theory test.

Write here

a)

b)

c)

9.2 Your work life skills, experiences, and achievements.

What is the good, beautiful, amazing, unique, or wonderful thing you want to achieve in the future in relation to your work life skills, experiences, and achievements?

Example:
Get promotion next year.

Write here

a)

b)

c)

How does this goal make you feel? Or, if it becomes a reality for you , how would you feel?

Example:

Success.

Write here

a)

b)

c)

What would you say of someone else who had this experience? What would this experience say about you as a person if it becomes a reality? How do you know this helpful self-label, belief, or voice to be true or what is the source of your evidence/ fact? *This is a chance to create a new helpful self-label, belief or voice to challenge any existing unhelpful self-label, belief, or voice.*

Example:

I'm an achiever.

Write here

a)

b)

c)

Action Points.
Is there any small step action you can or need to take to experience this good thing again or to experience a similar or a different good thing?

Example:

Book an appointment with my line manager to discuss my career.

Write here

a)

b)

c)

9.3 Your educational achievements/qualifications.

What is the good, beautiful, amazing, unique, or wonderful thing you want to achieve in the future in relation to your educational achievements/qualifications?

Example :

To complete an advanced course in staff supervision.

Write here

a)

b)

c)

How does this goal make you feel? Or, if it becomes a reality for you , how would you feel?

Example:

Satisfaction, secured.

Write here

a)

b)

c)

What would you say of someone else who had this experience? What would this experience say about you as a person if it becomes a reality? How do you know this helpful self-label, belief, or voice to be true or what is the source of your evidence/ fact? *This is a chance to create a new helpful self-label, belief or voice to challenge any existing unhelpful self-label, belief, or voice.*

Example:

I'm a determined person.

Write here

a)

b)

c)

Action Points.
Is there any small step action you can or need to take to experience this good thing again or to experience a similar or a different good thing?

Example:

Find the right supervision course and the fund and to book the course.

Write here

a)

b)

c)

9.4 Your work life skills, experiences, and achievements.

What is the good, beautiful, amazing, unique, or wonderful thing you want to achieve in the future in relation to your other skills, experiences and achievements not included above?

Example:

Play basketball with my family.

Write here

a)

b)

c)

How does this goal make you feel? Or, if it becomes a reality for you , how would you feel?

Example:

Team spirit, energetic.

Write here:

a)

b)

c)

What would you say of someone else who had this experience? What would this experience say about you as a person if it becomes a reality? How do you know this helpful self-label, belief, or voice to be true or what is the source of your evidence/ fact? *This is a chance to create a new helpful self-label, belief or voice to challenge any existing unhelpful self-label, belief, or voice.*

Example:

I'm a team player, an innovator of great ideas.

Write here

a)

b)

c)

Action Points.

Is there any small step action you can or need to take to experience this good thing again or to experience a similar or a different good thing?

Example:

To post on the family WhatsApp forum to trigger a conversation of the wellbeing and social benefits of setting up our extended family basketball team.

Write here

a)

b)

c)

9.5 Your family (parents) if any.

What is good, beautiful, amazing, unique, or wonderful about your family (parents) if any)?

Example:

A loving mum, who is an excellent cook and a business strategist. Dad is smart, caring and a courageous entrepreneur.

Write here

a)

b)

c)

How does this goal make you feel? Or, if it becomes a reality for you , how would I feel?

Example:

Confidence, hopeful.

Write here

a)

b)

c)

What would you say of someone else who had this experience? What would this experience say about you as a person if it becomes a reality? How do you know this helpful self-label, belief, or voice to be true or what is the source of your evidence/ fact? *This is a chance to create a new helpful self-label, belief or voice to challenge any existing unhelpful self-label, belief, or voice.*

Example:

Seek out beneficial opportunities.

Write here

a)

b)

c)

Action Points.
Is there any small step action you can or need to take to experience this good thing again or to experience a similar or a different good thing?

Example:

To make a record of mum's cooking recipes for my own use and for my children.

Write here

a)

b)

c)

9.6 Your family (children) if any.

What is good, beautiful, amazing, unique, or wonderful about your family (children) if any)?

Example:

Three angelic girls.

Write here

a)

b)

c)

How does this goal make you feel? Or, if it becomes a reality for you , how would I feel?

Example:

Affection, warmth

Write here

a)

b)

c)

What would you I say of someone else who had this experience? What would this experience say about you as a person if it becomes a reality? How do you know this helpful self-label, belief, or voice to be true or what is the source of your evidence/ fact? *This is a chance to create a new helpful self-label, belief or voice to challenge any existing unhelpful self-label, belief, or voice.*

Example:

A fortunate and wonderful parent.

Write here

a)

b)

c)

Action Points.
Is there any small step action you I can or need to take to experience this good thing again or to experience a similar or a different good thing?

Example:

Never stop telling my girls how precious they are and that they are stars irrespective of whatever anyone may say or whatever problem life may throw at them.

Write here

a)

b)

c)

9.7 Your other family members (if any).

What is good, beautiful, amazing, unique, or wonderful about your other family members (if any)?

Example:

A stubbornly brave late grandfather. A generous aunty still very active and kicking at age 86.

Write here

a)

b)

c)

How does this goal make me feel? Or, if it becomes a reality for you , how would you feel?

Example:

Unselfish, heroic.

Write here

a)

b)

c)

What would you say of someone else who had this experience? What would this experience say about you as a person if it becomes a reality? How do you know this helpful self-label, belief, or voice to be true or what is the source of your evidence/ fact? *This is a chance to create a new helpful self-label, belief or voice to challenge any existing unhelpful self-label, belief, or voice.*

Example:

A cub or a shoot of heroes and heroines.

Write here

a)

b)

c)

Action Points.

Is there any small step action you can or need to take to re-experience this good thing again or to experience a similar or a different good thing?

Example:

Visit aunty with my kids to listen to our family's heroic and adventurous stories.

Write here

a)

b)

c)

9.8 Your wife/husband/romantic partner (if any).

What is good, beautiful, amazing, unique, or wonderful about your romantic partner (if any)?

Example:

A cheerful, loyal, and caring wife.

Write here

a)

b)

c)

How does this goal make you feel? Or, if it becomes a reality for you , how would you feel?

Example:

Blessed, devoted.

Write here

a)

b)

c)

What would you say of someone else who had this experience? What would this experience say about you as a person if it becomes a reality? How do you know this helpful self-label, belief, or voice to be true or what is the source of your evidence/ fact? *This is a chance to create a new helpful self-label, belief or voice to challenge any existing unhelpful self-label, belief, or voice.*

Example:

I'm lucky.

Write here

a)

b)

c)

Action Points.
Is there any small step action you can or need to take to experience this good thing again or to experience a similar or a different good thing?

Example:

Tell my wife that she is glorious and a gift from heaven.

Write here

a)

b)

c)

9.9 Your friends/social network.

What is good, beautiful, amazing, unique, or wonderful about your friends/social network?

Example:

Hyacinth and Copsey have been enormous pastoral wellbeing support for me.

Write here

a)

b)

c)

How does this goal make you feel? Or, if it becomes a reality for you , how would you feel?

Example:

Friendship, grateful.

Write here

a)

b)

c)

What would you say of someone else who had this experience? What would this experience say about you as a person if it becomes a reality? How do you know this helpful self-label, belief, or voice to be true or what is the source of your evidence/ fact? *This is a chance to create a new helpful self-label, belief or voice to challenge any existing unhelpful self-label, belief, or voice.*

Example:

Able to receive and give care.

Write here

a)

b)

c)

Action Points.

Are there any small step action you can or need to take to experience this good thing again or to experience a similar or a different good thing?

Example

To accept to mentor one young person.

Write here

a)

b)

c)

9.10 Things/qualities people appreciate about you. Other people's good view of you.

What things/qualities people appreciate about you ? Other people's good view of you?

Example:

My manager said I'm the most experienced and skilled therapist in our health service. The head of department of a former health organisation I worked for, wrote to a professional regulator that I'm an exceptionally intelligent person.

Write here

a)

b)

c)

How does this goal make you feel? Or, if it becomes a reality for you , how would you feel?

Example:

Self-worth, Inspire.

Write here

a)

b)

c)

What would you say of someone else who had this experience? What would this experience say about you as a person if it becomes a reality? How do you know this helpful self-label, belief, or voice to be true or what is the source of your evidence/fact? *This is a chance to create a new helpful self-label, belief or voice to challenge any existing unhelpful self-label, belief, or voice.*

Example:

I'm intelligent, skilled, and experienced.

Write here

a)

b)

c)

Action Points.

Is there any small step action you can or need to take to experience this good thing again or to experience a similar or a different good thing?

Example:

To make a note of and sit on the emotions (at least once a week) from the positive feedback people gave me.

Write here

a)

b)

c)

9.11 Nature in relation to plants/trees.

What is good, beautiful, amazing, unique, or wonderful about plants/trees?

Example:

The apricot and the apple trees in my back garden started fruiting this year.

Write here

a)

b)

c)

How does this goal make you feel? Or, if it becomes a reality for you , how would you feel?

Example:

Wonders of nature, delicious.

Write here

a)

b)

c)

What would you say of someone else who had this experience? What would this experience say about you as a person if it becomes a reality? How do you know this helpful self-label, belief, or voice to be true or what is the source of your evidence/ fact? *This is a chance to create a new helpful self-label, belief or voice to challenge any existing unhelpful self-label, belief, or voice.*

Example:

I can make my dreams come true.

Write here

a)

b)

c)

Action Points.
Is there any small step action you can or need to take to experience this good thing again or to experience a similar or a different good thing?

Example:

Invest at least two hours a month in gardening and tendering my fruit plants and crops.

Write here

a)

b)

c)

9.12 Nature in relation to animals.

What is good, beautiful, amazing, unique, or wonderful about nature in relation to animals?

Example:

Birds singing in my garden and neighbourhood.

Write here

a)

b)

c)

How does this goal make you feel? Or, if it becomes a reality for you , how would you feel?

Example:

Thrilled, relaxed.

Write here

a)

b)

d)

What would you say of someone else who had this experience? What would this experience say about you as a person if it becomes a reality? How do you know this helpful self-label, belief, or voice to be true or what is the source of your evidence/ fact? *This is a chance to create a new helpful self-label, belief or voice to challenge any existing unhelpful self-label, belief, or voice.*

Example:

I'm a lover of beautiful bird songs.

Write here

a)

b)

c)

Action Points.
Is there any small step action you can or need to take to experience this good thing again or to experience a similar or a different good thing?

Example:

To listen to bird's singing as part of my meditation and mindfulness practice.

Write here

a)

b)

c)

9.13 Nature in relation to climate.

What is good, beautiful, amazing, unique, or wonderful about nature in relation to climate?

Example:

Fresh air from rain shower after days of intense hot weather and dry air.

Write here

a)

b)

c)

How does this goal make you feel? Or, if it becomes a reality for you , how would I feel?

Example:

Serene, refreshing.

Write here

a)

b)

c)

What would you say of someone else who had this experience? What would this experience say about you as a person if it becomes a reality? How do you know this helpful self-label, belief, or voice to be true or what is the source of your evidence/ fact? *This is a chance to create a new helpful self-label, belief or voice to challenge any existing unhelpful self-label, belief, or voice.*

Example:

I can find healing from nature.

Write here

a)

b)

c)

Action Points.
Is there any small step action you can or need to take to experience this good thing again or to experience a similar or a different good thing?

Example:

To deliberately go for a walk to enjoy fresh air.

Write here

a)

b)

c)

9.14 Nature in relation to other aspects of nature you wish to experience or interact with.

What is good, beautiful, amazing, unique, or wonderful about nature in relation to other aspects of nature you wish to experience or interact with?

Example:

Watch ducklings swimming or visit a sea beach.

Write here

a)

b)

c)

How does this goal make you feel? Or, if it becomes a reality for you , how would you feel?

Example:

Thrilled, discovering.

Write here

a)

b)

c)

What would you say of someone else who had this experience? What would this experience say about you as a person if it becomes a reality? How do you know this helpful self-label, belief, or voice to be true or what is the source of your evidence/ fact? *This is a chance to create a new helpful self-label, belief or voice to challenge any existing unhelpful self-label, belief, or voice.*

Example:

I'm adventurous.

Write here

a)

b)

c)

Action Points.

Is there any small step action you can or need to take to experience this good thing again or to experience a similar or a different good thing?

Example:

Go to a park to watch ducklings.

Write here

a)

b)

c)

9.15 What's next?

Now that you have worked through this section, you should pause and reflect on your answers. Put the book aside for a few minutes before answering the questions below

☐ What have you learned and achieved from this section?

_____

_____

_____

☐ What self-help coping techniques do you want to learn?

_____

_____

_____

☐ Are there any questions you would like to ask medical professionals?

_____

_____

_____

☐ What specific self-improvement goal or achievement do you want to set for yourself for the next week?

_____

_____

_____

It may be useful to provide yourself with at least five minutes a week to regularly review and reflect on your self-improvement goal. If you do not set aside time to take care of your wellbeing, the daily demands of life may overwhelm you, and it will become harder to develop self-help techniques.

Do not ignore your well-being because life is not endless here on earth. Try to do at least one small act of kindness, compassion, or self-care for yourself today.

My Review Date _____ Time _____ Place _____

9.16 Your Feedback.

The Twin Brain Project Team would like to hear from you if you have helpful suggestions that could help them to improve any aspect of this section for other users. Email your suggestions to admin@twinbrain.org. Please copy info@healthbj-uk.org into your email to make sure your feedback is received. Thank you in advance for helping to improve the Twin Brain resource .

Chapter 10
THE CALMING TECHNIQUES OVERVIEW

10.1 How will calming techniques help me?

▶ They help to improve sleep, reduce anxiety, and reduce replay of unhelpful trauma memories by creating calmness.

▶ Ongoing practice as you would in a gym exercise is needed to gradually become good with your techniques and before they can become life skills for spontaneous use by the brain.

10.2 How do calming techniques work?

Think of the brain as a big organization or country with the front being its President, Prime Minister, Queen or King who manages information and makes big plans and decisions. There is a small organ (amygdala) overseeing security. The President received information from the security team that the world is on fire and there is trouble. The President passed the information to the Chief Security Officer e(amygdala). The Chief Security Officer presses the emergency alarm for protection of the citizens. The Chief Security Officer oversees the attack, defence, or escape method. The President needs to be taken to safety. Other soldiers are asked to stop their routine duties and to re-direct all their resources and efforts to protect from the danger.

Brain of Emotions

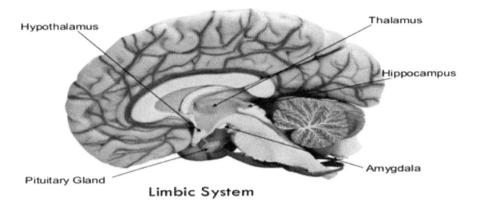

Source/Acknowledged: Rizzolatti, G., & Sinigaglia, C. (2008): Mirrors in the brain

It does not matter if the information is wrong - once the alarm goes off, the stress hormones (cortisone) are produced. When the amygdala is busy protecting us, it pulls resources from other units of the brain by shutting down or reducing their functions/ activities. Therefore, you do not think about food, laughter, play, physical intimacy in times of anxiety or crisis.

When doing a calming technique, you are trying to re-awaken the brain's President (front brain) so that you can think, plan, and make good decisions immediately. Thinking, planning, and decision making may be suspended or reduced when we are anxious or in a perceived or real threatening situation.

How true is this for you at the moment? If yes, why? If no, why?

_____

_____

_____

10.3 List of Calming Techniques Part One.

These techniques are covered in this Chapter of this book

 a). Counting numbers and alphabets backwards.

 b). Naming objects.

 c). Discriminating between the past and the present.

 d). Breathing with rhyme or rhymical breathing.

 e). Sensory touching/soothing.

 f). Deep muscles relaxation.

 g). Stress bucket imagery.

 h). Pink elegant imagery or pushing a ball under water exercise.

 i). Under the rain exercise.

 j). Noisy passengers on bus imagery.

 k). Index finger pointing exercise.

 l). Bamboo pipe finger exercise.

 m).Horse on thin chair imagery.

 n). Don't ever give up imagery.

10.4 List of Calming Techniques Part Two.

These techniques are covered in the next Chapter of this book

 a). Safe trip.

 b). Mindfulness and Attention focusing.

10.5 What's next?

Now that you have worked through this section, you should pause and reflect on your answers. Put the book aside for a few minutes before answering the questions below

☐ What have you learned and achieved from this section?

_____

_____

_____

☐ What self-help coping techniques do you want to learn?

_____

_____

_____

☐ Are there any questions you would like to ask medical professionals?

_____

_____

_____

☐ What specific self-improvement goal or achievement do you want to set for yourself for the next week?

_____

_____

_____

It may be useful to provide yourself with at least five minutes a week to regularly review and reflect on your self-improvement goal. If you do not set aside time to take care of your wellbeing, the daily demands of life may overwhelm you, and it will become harder to develop self-help techniques.

Do not ignore your well-being because life is not endless here on earth. Try to do at least one small act of kindness, compassion, or self-care for yourself today.

My Review Date _____ **Time** _____ **Place** _____

10.6 Your Feedback.

The Twin Brain Project Team would like to hear from you if you have helpful suggestions that could help them to improve any aspect of this section for other users. Email your suggestions to admin@twinbrain.org. Please copy info@healthbj-uk.org into your email to make sure your feedback is received. Thank you in advance for helping to improve the Twin Brain resource.

Chapter 11
CALMING TECHNIQUES PART ONE

Health & Happy

11.1 List of Calming Techniques Part One.

These techniques are covered in this Chapter of this book

- a). Counting numbers and alphabets backwards.
- b). Naming objects.
- c). Discriminating between the past and the present.
- d). Breathing with rhyme or rhymical breathing.
- e). Sensory touching/soothing.
- f). Deep muscles relaxation.
- g). Stress bucket imagery.
- h). Pink elegant imagery or pushing a ball under water exercise.
- i). Under the rain exercise.

j). Noisy passengers on bus imagery.

k). Index finger pointing exercise.

l). Bamboo pipe finger exercise.

m).Horse on thin chair imagery.

n). Don't ever give up imagery.

11.2 Counting Numbers and Alphabets Backwards.

ZYXWVUTS
RQPONMLK
JIHGFEDCBA

a). Counting numbers backwards

▶ Counting few numbers backwards in English or in your preferred language from '5, 4, 3, 2, 1, 0'.

How did it feel doing this exercise? Was it difficult or easy? If yes, why? If no, why?

_____

_____

_____

▶ Counting more numbers backwards in English or in your preferred language from '10, 9...to 0'.

How did it feel doing this exercise? Was it difficult or easy? If yes, why? If no, why?

_____

_____

_____

- Counting many numbers backwards in English or in your preferred language from '50, 49...to 0'.

How did it feel doing this exercise? Was it difficult or easy? If yes, why? If no, why?

_____

_____

_____

- Counting many numbers backwards in English or in your preferred language from '100, 99, 98...to 0'.

How did it feel doing this exercise? Was it difficult or easy? If yes, why? If no, why?

_____

_____

_____

b). Counting alphabets backwards

- Counting few alphabets backwards from 'D, C, B, A'.

How did it feel doing this exercise? Was it difficult or easy? If yes, why? If no, why?

_____

_____

_____

- Counting more alphabets backwards from 'G, F...to A'.

How did it feel doing this exercise? Was it difficult or easy? If yes, why? If no, why?

_____

_____

_____

_____

_____

❭ Counting larger alphabets backwards from 'K, J...to A'.

How did it feel doing this exercise? Was it difficult or easy? If yes, why? If no, why?

_____

_____

_____

❭ Counting larger alphabets backwards from "Z, Y....to A'.

How did it feel doing this exercise? Was it difficult or easy? If yes, why? If no, why?

_____

_____

_____

c). Why counting alphabets backwards creates calm?

For the human brain, the counting of alphabets backwards is like having someone doing some work in your garden.

You say to the gardener 'I have one hour for you. I'm going to pay you 10 pounds for the hour.'

20 minutes later, you are outside and the gardener is on the phone chatting rather than working.

What would you say to this gardener?

Example

I ask 'What have you done so far?'
They reply 'I've finished with the flowers'.

_____

_____

_____

You may ask the gardener to clean up the fallen leaves. 10 minutes later the gardener is on their phone again and the excuse is that they finished the last activity. This time around you give him a list of every activity that you need him to do in your garden. Example, watering the plants, then the next task and the next task until the one hour you are paying for is finished.

The idea is that if the gardener is smart enough that after you tell them once or twice about tasks they should do, they should use their initiative to go ahead to do the next task and the task after until the agreed time is finished.

The brain is like the gardener. If you want to count from number '10 to 0' or the alphabet 'E to A' the brain will give you the number '10' or the alphabet 'E' and it will want to return to the anxiety or the replay of unhelpful memories or thoughts. The brain sees the anxiety or the unhelpful memories or thoughts as a priority because of the need to protect us. If you keep counting, at some point the brain will reduce or let go of some of the anxiety or the unhelpful memories or thoughts. Some of the resources the brain invested in keeping the anxiety or the memories or thoughts are being used to help the brain to keep counting the numbers or alphabets.

Counting happens at the forebrain and anxiety happens at the amygdala. So, there are two jobs. The amygdala and the forebrain, like good humans must come to some compromise. If we helped to re-awaken the forebrain, it will take back its executive planning and decision-making role and shut down the amygdala.

How true is this for you at the moment? If yes, why? If no, why?

_____

_____

_____

How did it feel doing this exercise? Was it difficult or easy? If yes, why? If no, why?

_____

_____

_____

11.3 Naming Objects.

Look around where you are right now. What do you see? Call out or write down a list of everything you see. You can name objects/ things around you and described each in detail before moving to the next object. This can be loud and verbal or a written list and if you want to, even if you are to repeat the list over and over.

Example

- ❯ A phone inside a red leader cover. It has white edges and a new transparent screen protector. There is a magnetic self-lock.
- ❯ A blue coffee box with a round lid. The inside gold coloured. It has a rough edge all around the bottom.
- ❯ A paper tissues pack. It's rectangular, yellow, and soft.
- ❯ A black jacket hanging on a stand.
- ❯ A pink lamb with two white light bulbs. It has a long silver stand sitting on a large and a heavy round base.
- ❯ A peacock picture on the wall. It's square and it has a beautiful photo of a dancing or rejoicing peacock.

How did it feel doing this exercise? Was it difficult or easy? If yes, why? If no, why?

_____

_____

_____

Why Naming Objects creates calm?

- It requires you to move your head to face the object (e.g., desk or phone) you want to name.
- The eyes will take video and photo shots of images.
- The ears will listen.
- The brain will be thinking about each object – its size, shape, colour etc.
- The muscles of the mouth must cooperate with the brain's instruction or message to allow verbal description of each object you are naming. We do not know how many actions and units of the brain involved. To name one object, it takes time and multiple layers of actions by the brain.
- It involves multiple activities happening within the brain and other parts of the body. They work together in what appears to be a perfect unity or partnership. If one unit of the brain or the body refuses or fails to cooperate in teamwork, then confusion follows.

Example

- If we did not have enough sleep the previous night, in the morning the body may feel tired and the brain struggles to stay focused on tasks (concentration).
- If the tongue is infected, we can't talk at all or not properly.

How true is this for you at the moment? If yes, why? If no, why?

_____

_____

_____

_____

95

- For example, you name and say *'that is a table'* then *'that is a gas boiler'*, *'that is a fan'*, *'that is a fridge'* etc until there are no more objects to name and you may start all over again until you feel tired and stop. The brain must decide either to help you keep naming objects or to keep focusing on the worrying thing.
- The naming happens within the forebrain and the anxiety happens within amygdala.

How did it feel doing this exercise? Was it difficult or easy? If yes, why? If no, why?

_____

_____

_____

11.4 Breathing with Rhythm or Rhythmical Breathing.

This technique is about flow. The older generation of mothers have been using this technique without being taught the science behind it. They use it to help babies to go to sleep because the brain responds to rhythm (when something happens steadily over and over, like a drumbeat), for example when the baby is rocked gently by the parent. When a child is crying or screaming, their brain waves spike up and down. When there is music or singing, it brings the waves calm down gradually and that calms down the child.

The question is, what is it about breathing with rhythm? There is something about rhythm that calms the body down.

This technique can be practised with or without music or dance. When you are feeling anxious, your brain is looking for danger inside your body or your environment. On a computer screen, the brain waves go up and down like a stormy sea. Exercises that use rhythm calm down the brain quickly and you feel calmer. Music or dance or hand movements are likely to produce similar effect on the brain and body.

Breathing those rhymes or with rhythm can be practised with real or visualised movement of your hand up and down. You can also visualise a swing swinging in a park.

Exercise

- ▶ I want you to slowly breathe in as your right hand slowly goes up.
- ▶ Slowly breathe out as your hand comes down.
- ▶ You must breathe at your own pace and ensure you do not hurt yourself in anyway.
- ▶ Stop the exercise whenever you want to stop.
- ▶ You can practise few minutes.
- ▶ If you want, you may close your eyes, sit back, relax and do it or you may stand and eyes open.
- ▶ You may use the raising up and down of your hand or anything that moves. For example, you could imagine a swing at the park.

How did it feel doing this exercise? Was it difficult or easy? If yes, why? If no, why?

11.5 Sensory Touching.

It is touching, gentle rub or a squeeze of a part of your body to feel and realise that you are alive, you are here and now, you are not in some distant places, you are not in the past. It's like when we are sleeping, or daydreaming, somebody touches us: we just wake up and come back to reality.

You can rub your ring or an elastic band against your skin and see what you feel. Some people rub their hands. The idea is that we need to wake up from the anxiety or that state of a daze. We need a physical touch of our skin to bring us back to consciousness in a very real way, I am here, and this is me. I'm alive, I'm not sleeping. It may be more effective to touch the same spot regularly to help the brain to associate or link the touching to the need to snap out of the anxious dreaming state.

For example, a gentle tickle or rub of a specific spot of your skin, ear, hand etc to feel the tingling that awakens you from sleep or trance like state that the body may enter during anxiety.

Other examples drink refreshing water, tapping your head, touching your ear etc.

_____

_____

_____

During period of anxiety or a replay of trauma/painful memories, the brain may behave as if it is jumped backward or forward in time travelling to a place or a moment of past or future bad experience. Sometimes you feel anxious when you remember the past. Sometimes you feel sweaty or tension over an interview that is in the future and has not occurred.

How true is this for you at the moment? If yes, why? If no, why?

_____

_____

_____

How did it feel doing this exercise? Was it difficult or easy? If yes, why? If no, why?

_____

_____

_____

11.6 Discriminating Between the Past and Present.

This technique is close to the sensory touching technique because it reminds the brain to awake from dream state and to be here and now. It is a training for the brain to recognise the difference between the past and the present. Sometimes, the brain mixes up memories and could not tell what happened 3 or 6 months ago from what is happening now. Even if events look alike, it does not make them the same.

Example, if a person was attacked in the evening by someone wearing a white pair of shoes and a green jacket. The brain may conclude that every evening and anyone wearing a white pair of shoes and a green jacket is dangerous. This may lead to avoidance of going out in the evening or staying away or feeling suspicious of people with white pair of shoes and a green jacket.

How true is this for you at the moment? If yes, why? If no, why?

_____

_____

_____

You can teach your brain to tell the differences between some specific things for the time the original event happened and the now. Do not use things that are too a like to practise discrimination because it may make the bad memories or anxiety worst. Things that are too similar remind the brain of the original bad event.

Examples

▶ Your age then and now.

Age 7 versus 35

_____

_____

_____

▶ Your location then and now.

Walking through a local Park in Paris, France versus sitting and watching TV news in my room in London UK or Yorkshire UK versus Hythe UK.

▶ What you were wearing then and now.

White sporting shoes, a blue T-shirt, and a yellow cap etc versus black leader shoes, long brown sleeves, and a brown jacket.

▶ Job then and now.

Primary school pupil versus a management consultant.

▶ Marital status then and now.
A child versus married and has a child of my own.

▶ Who was I with then and who am I with now?
My attacker versus with my work colleagues.

How did it feel doing this exercise? Was it difficult or easy? If yes, why? If no, why?

_____

_____

11.7 Deep Muscles Relaxation.

It is creating massage feeling by squeezing and releasing different parts of your body. To do that, you pay attention to your body to see which parts you feel positive sensation and which parts you feel pain, discomfort, or nothing. In the future, you may like to do the exercise only on those parts of your body where you feel positive sensation. Avoid parts of the body that you feel pain, discomfort, or nothing. You may sit, stand, or use any body position comfortable for you.

_____

_____

- ▶ Squeeze your toes as if you are grabbing the floor. Feel the muscles tension of your toes as if you are trying to massage your legs. When you are tired with the squeeze, then release the squeeze.
- ▶ Do the exercise on your lower legs up to hips together, arms, arms, and the whole hands together. Your bottom up through your back to shoulders and neck.

- Do the exercise on your chest and shoulders by squeezing backward and forward.
- Do the exercise on your upper shoulders through the neck to the whole of your head.
- Do the exercise simultaneously on the whole of your body from toes to head. You may want to stand, sit, or keep a body position comfortable for you. You may gently (do not hurt yourself) bend sideway left, sideway right, backward towards your back and forward towards your chest.

You may only be able to squeeze and release some body parts under some situations. Examples, if you are doing this exercise while sitting with your legs under a table or if you are driving a car.

How did it feel doing this exercise? Was it difficult or easy? If yes, why? If no, why?

_____

_____

_____

11.8 Stress Bucket Imagery.

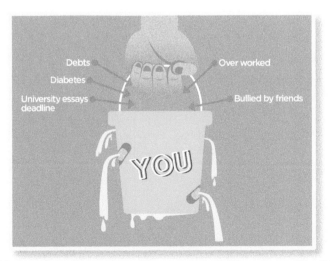

Source/Acknowledgement: Hopscotch & Harmony Pty Ltd, 2022:
Child, Teen & Adult Psychology.
Brabban & Turkington, 2022: Stress and vulnerability Bucket.

Imagery is what you see when you think of something. For example, when I write 'horse' you will think of what a horse looks like. This is imagery.

If you have a bucket with lots of holes, how would you fill it with water? More water is being poured into it by you or other people and it simply leaking away from the holes. You are the bucket – if you are full of holes to an extent that you cannot keep your energy and motivation in, and others who try to fill your bucket cannot do it either.

How true is this for you at the moment? If yes, why? If no, why?

_____

_____

_____

Possible Solutions.
- Identify or mark the situation as stressful or worrying.
- Talk to someone in a safe space about how you are feeling.
- Ask for resource support.
- Talk to the people who are adding to your stress bucket that you no longer have capacity to take on more.
- Improve or increase your ability to plan and prioritise tasks.
- Increase your self-care activities, including holiday or work time breaks, exercises, social interactions etc. That is, never forget to add petrol or fuel to your life engine because things may ground to a halt.
- Eating healthy and getting enough sleep.
- Challenge or reinterpret unhelpful thinking around your beliefs about doing too many tasks or taking too many responsibilities from people at the expense of your wellbeing.

How did it feel doing this exercise? Was it difficult or easy? If yes, why? If no, why?

_____

_____

_____

11.9 Pink Elegant or Pushing a Ball Under Water Imagery.

The idea is that if you try so hard to avoid a particular thought, the brain may become curious with what you are trying to avoid or hide.

For example

What happens if I say to you 'try to avoid thinking of a pink elephant'?
How did it feel doing this exercise? Was it difficult or easy? If yes, why? If no, why?

_____

_____

_____

_____

It is like trying hard to push a ball under the water and it keeps popping back up to the surface . Sometimes it may be helpful to accept that an unwanted or invited thought is there but get on with your daily life.

11.10 Under the Rain Imagery.

This technique is about deliberately not allowing some aspects of your daily life to stop because of a problem you are currently facing.

For example,

If you are walking home and it suddenly rained and you get wet. What would you do?

_____

_____

_____

☐ You may choose to stop in the rain, get angry and shout at the rain. Yet you are still wet and not at home, OR

How true may this be for you at the moment? If yes, why? If no, why?

_____

_____

_____

☐ You may choose to remind yourself that the rain is not a person and it isn't trying to upset you. You can remind yourself to carry an umbrella next time. For today it is okay to walk home wet and still arrive home if there is nowhere to escape the rain.

How true may this be for you at the moment? If yes, why? If no, why?

_____

_____

_____

11.11 Finger Trap Exercise.

Source author: Unknown but acknowledged

This technique involves putting one of your five fingers into the hole of the finger trap. You try to remove your finger carefully and tenderly from the hole.

How did it feel doing this exercise? Was it difficult or easy? If yes, why? If no, why?

_____

_____

_____

If you are stressed and tensed, the bamboo will hold your finger and it will sink deeper into the bamboo. This technique reminds you to be more relaxed and flexible with your daily life.

How true may this be for you at the moment? If yes, why? If no, why?

_____

_____

_____

11.12 Noisy Passengers on Bus or Train Imagery.

Source author: Unknown but acknowledged

This technique is about deliberately not allowing people or some aspects of your daily life to stop because of a problem you are currently facing.

For example,

If you are the driver of a public bus and there is one noisy passenger, and you cannot get this person off the bus , what would you do?

_____

_____

_____

_____

You may

☐ Stop the [train] or bus and get angry. You and other passengers get angry because he is making you late OR

How true is this for you at the moment? If yes, why? If no, why?

_____

_____

_____

☐ Keep driving and stay focused on your destination until the Police arrive to take the noisy passenger off your bus or [train].

How true is this for you at the moment? If yes, why? If no, why?

_____

_____

_____

11.13 Horse on a Thin Chair Imagery.

Source author: Unknown but acknowledged

This imagery is a reminder that some problems are not real, we have just decided that they are. Our brain tries to tell us bad things that happened in the past are happening now or will happen. This is called conditioning.

How true is this for you at the moment? If yes, why? If no, why?

_____

_____

_____

If we take safe and small steps to walk away or run away, the world will not come to an end.

How true is this for you at the moment? If yes, why? If no, why?

_____

_____

_____

11.14 Don't Ever Give Up Imagery.

Source author: Unknown but acknowledged

This imagery is a reminder that we can either seek the help of an expert (such as a doctor or therapist) or keep trying to solve the problem, and never stop trying. Never give up hope!

How true is this for you at the moment? If yes, why? If no, why?

_____

_____

_____

11.15 What's next?

Now that you have worked through this section, you should pause and reflect on your answers. Put the book or a pp aside for a few minutes before answering the questions below

☐ What have you learned and achieved from this section?

Example

There are many exercises I can do to reduce my stress and anxiety and to feel calmer. Example, breathing exercise.

_____

_____

_____

☐ What self-help coping techniques do you want to learn?

Example

Discrimination technique, pink elephant imagery, etc.

_____

_____

_____

☐ Are there any questions you would like to ask medical professionals?

Example

There are so many calming techniques, so which one to pick and practise long term?

_____

_____

_____

☐ What specific self-improvement goal or achievement do you want to set for yourself for the next week?

Example

To do breathing exercise for 2 minutes at least once on Wednesday 25, August 2021, 12pm and Saturday 28. August 2021, 12pm.

_____

_____

_____

It may be useful to provide yourself with at least five minutes a week to regularly review and reflect on your self-improvement goal. If you do not set aside time to take care of your wellbeing, the daily demands of life may overwhelm you, and it will become harder to develop self-help techniques.

Do not ignore your well-being because life is not endless here on earth. Try to do at least one small act of kindness, compassion, or self-care for yourself today.

My Review Date _____ **Time** _____ **Place** _____

11.15 Your Feedback.

The Twin Brain Project Team would like to hear from you if you have helpful suggestions that could help them to improve any aspect of this section for other users. Email your suggestions to admin@twinbrain.org. Please copy info@healthbj-uk.org into your email to make sure your feedback is received. Thank you in advance for helping to improve the Twin Brain resource.

Chapter 12

In this chapter, we are going to look at three more techniques which help us appreciate the present and stay positive.

▶ 'Safe Trip'
▶ Attention Focusing
▶ Mindfulness

12.1 'Safe Trip'.

The human brain appears to have the ability to 'time travel' back in time and allows us to remember the past. However sometimes it gets stuck in negative memories.

How true is this for you at the moment? If yes, why? If no, why?

_____

_____

_____

The 'Safe Trip' exercise is used to time travel to a peaceful, beautiful, or safe psychological room, space, or a moment in your history. This helps the brain feel positive emotions and bodily reactions as if we are back in that old situation.

How true is this for you at the moment? If yes, why? If no, why?

_____

_____

_____

To do a 'Safe Trip'

- ▶ You simply close your eyes.
- ▶ Relax and count from 0 to 10.
- ▶ Think of the positive memory of your choice.
- ▶ Or you can look at a picture or watch a video to help to take you back to the memory of your choice.
- ▶ Try to avoid going into memories that are negative during your safe trip. Recognise you are thinking an unhelpful thought, and let it drift away, and focus on the positive memory again.

114

- You can use a stopwatch or alarm to end the memory session.

How did it feel doing this exercise? Was it difficult or easy? If yes, why? If no, why?

_____

_____

_____

12.2 Attention Focusing.

Attention focusing and mindfulness (see below) train your brain to pay attention. Attention focusing and mindfulness do this in different ways, but they complement one another so you should practise both if you can.

Attention focusing is about
- Being curious and having a desire to know more about yourself or about something.
- Training the brain to pay attention, be in one place, fixed on one activity, going into details, be precise and think more deeply.
- Using the five senses to help you recognise and describe what you are experiencing. The five senses are smell (nose), sight (eyes), touch (skin), taste (tongue) and hearing (ears).

How true is this for you at the moment? If yes, why? If no, why?

_____

_____

_____

Why attention focusing creates calm?

▶ When you focus your attention on certain things, your brain has less time to create anxious or worried negative thoughts.

▶ If you are busy observing details with the five senses and describing verbally or writing down as many details as you can, your brain also is less likely have time to think about something else that is bothering you.

▶ During that period of attention focusing, your brain has no choice but to reduce or stop the anxiety.

▶ If you are experiencing trauma flashbacks or memories the brain will reduce, stop, or suspend the flashback or memory.

▶ If you are struggling to sleep, you may find that when you think of all the details during the attention focusing exercise, the brain may drift off into sleep mode.

How true is this for you at the moment? If yes, why? If no, why?

_____

_____

_____

_____

_____

_____

12.3 Imagine a 5-year-old child looking at a lady bird.

You should pay attention to little children and see how well they focus their attention focusing and mindfulness. Most adults lose this ability – they forget to stop and appreciate the details of small, normal things. This means they drift away from living mindfully and focusing their attention.

How true is this for you at the moment? If yes, why? If no, why?

_____

_____

_____

For example

A therapist and five children were walking through a field of beautiful flowers on a sunny afternoon. The children were aged between 3 and 10. The therapist noticed the youngest child (age 3) walked into the field and among the flowers and the grasses. The therapist called out to this child to come back. The child did not answer or come back but used his/her hands to invite the group to come and see. The therapist and the older children rushed to the child in a bit of panic and saw that the child was looking at a ladybird. The child was amazed by the ladybird and had a big smile on his/her face!

117

Why do you think the older children and the therapist walked through the same field and did not notice the ladybird? How come the youngest child was the only person able to notice a lady bird insect deep inside the grasses?

_____

_____

_____

12.4 Practice Guide.

Use your five senses to observe and describe verbally loud or in writing what you are experiencing in the practice examples below

12.4.1 Practice example A sweet orange or a tangerine fruit.

If you are peeling a sweet orange or a tangerine fruit with your fingernails, focus your attention on the physical act of peeling it, paying attention to how precise you are, and making sure that every skin of the orange or the tangerine is peeled.

   a). What are you smelling with your nose?

_____

_____

_____

   b). What are you seeing with your eyes?

_____

_____

_____

   c). What are you feeling or sensing with your skin?

_____

_____

_____

d). What are you tasting or noticing with your tongue?

_____

_____

_____

e). What are you hearing with your ears?

_____

_____

_____

In this example ,

- ▶ Mindfulness could be stopping, sitting down and relaxing with a piece of the peeled orange or the tangerine in your mouth.
- ▶ Being aware of the orange or the tangerine juice on your tongue dripping very slowly down your throat.
- ▶ Stay there, do nothing and just enjoy the taste and the moment.

How did it feel doing this exercise? Was it difficult or easy? If yes, why? If no, why?

_____

_____

_____

12.4.2 Practice Example A Clock or Wristwatch with Moving Hands.

Is there a clock or watch near you? Watch the two hands. Are they moving? You may not be able to use all the five senses, but if the clock is making a sound, you can use your sense of hearing. You cannot use the tongue to taste because it is not appropriate. But you can still do some form of attention focusing by describing the clock in detail as much as possible. One way to do that is probably not to look at it, but describe how much you remember

a). What is the texture (you can touch it with your fingers)?

_____

_____

b). What is the colour?

_____

_____

c). What is the design?

_____

_____

d). What is the type of leather (if any)?

_____

_____

e). Is it Roman capitals or numbers or English alphabets?

_____

_____

Later look at the clock or wristwatch to see how much you got correct..

How did it feel doing this exercise? Was it difficult or easy? If yes, why? If no, why?

_____

_____

_____

☐ This exercise reminds you how much attention you pay to things around you. When we become too busy with bigger things and too familiar to our environment, we begin to lose or miss the small really important details around us. The more precise you can describe the clock, will remind you how good you are with attention focusing.

How true is this for you at the moment? If yes, why? If no, why?

_____

_____

_____

☐ If you are paying attention to things around you, you should be able to describe your clock in as much detail as possible. If you struggle to get it right, it reminds you that probably you are not paying attention to things around you as much as you should.

How true is this for you at the moment? If yes, why? If no, why?

_____

_____

_____

12.4.3 Index Finger Exercise as Attention Focusing Gone Wrong.

Look at your index finger. Can you put your index finger in front of your face between your two eyes? How good is your visibility?

_____

_____

_____

If you remove or lower your index finger from the front of your eyes, how good will your sight be?

_____

_____

_____

The purpose of this exercise is that when we have a problem and allow it to consume us, it can become like the index finger in front of our eyes. [and in front of our daily lives.] It begins to cloud our vision of life and other real priorities.

How true is this for you at the moment? If yes, why? If no, why?

_____

_____

_____

_____

❑ What will it be like if you are walking on a very busy street with your index finger in front of your eyes? How good will your vision be?

_____

_____

_____

We begin to collide and bump into things and other people . We begin to get distracted from things that are important.

How true is this for you at the moment? If yes, why? If no, why?

_____

_____

_____

When the brain becomes too focused and worrying on something, it begins to go into many details about that thing. This is not bad , but it's not what we want. At that point it means the brain is putting too much resource into the thing it is focusing on. We begin to get distracted and the brain forgets that there are other important things to do. It is about being aware of what unimportant things the brain is doing and find something more important for the brain to do. Be aware that whatever the problem or issue you are experiencing right now, when you allow it to become the index finger, it begins to cause trouble by causing you to begin to bump around physically or emotionally and you get distracted from the important or beautiful things in life.

How true is this for you at the moment? If yes, why? If no, why?

_____

_____

_____

_____

_____

12.5 What's next?

Now that you have worked through this section, you should pause and reflect on your answers. Put the book aside for a few minutes before answering the questions below

☐ What have you learned and achieved from this section?

_____

_____

_____

☐ What self-help coping techniques do you want to learn?

_____

_____

_____

☐ Are there any questions you would like to ask medical professionals?

_____

_____

_____

☐ What specific self-improvement goal or achievement do you want to set for yourself for the next week?

_____

_____

_____

It may be useful to provide yourself with at least five minutes twice week to regularly review and reflect on your self-improvement goal. If you do not set aside time to take care of your wellbeing, the daily demands of life may overwhelm you, and it will become harder to develop self-help techniques.

Do not ignore your well-being because life is not endless here on earth. Try to do at least one small act of kindness, compassion, or self-care for yourself today.

My Review Date _____ **Time** _____ **Place** _____

The Twin Brain Project Team would like to hear from you if you have helpful suggestions that could help them to improve any aspect of this section for other users. Email your suggestions to admin@twinbrain.org. Please copy info@healthbj-uk.org into your email to make sure your feedback is received. Thank you in advance for helping to improve the Twin Brain resource.

Chapter 13
OTHER EXAMPLES TO FOCUS YOUR ATTENTION

Below we have provided a few other examples you could use to focus your attention. Try to notice all the details about the object you are holding, or thing you are doing. Use the examples below to practise – you can imagine each object and try to think of all the details, or you can use the actual objects to practise with the five senses of smell (nose), sight (eyes), touch (skin), taste (tongue) and hearing (ears).

Note *You must keep safe and do not hurt yourself or someone else. For example, you should not taste a very hot coffee that will burn your tongue.*

13.1 Tea or coffee e.g. *Do you like to drink tea or coffee? Do you use milk, sugar etc? If you tap the cup, what sound would you hear?*

How did it feel doing this exercise? Was it difficult or easy? If yes, why? If no, why?

_____

_____

_____

13.2 Glass of water e.g. *What shape is the glass? What colour is the glass? How does the water taste? Is it nice and refreshing, or too cold? When you tap the glass what sound does it make?*

How did it feel doing this exercise? Was it difficult or easy? If yes, why? If no, why?

_____

_____

_____

13.3 Kitchen sink and washing plates/dishes e.g. *When was the last time you washed plates in your kitchen sink? You will not be able to use your sense of taste in this situation (licking dirty dishes isn't very hygienic!), but you can use your other senses. You can hear the noises of the plates, smell the washing liquid/soap, see the bubbles from the washing liquid floating away and bursting etc.*

How did it feel doing this exercise? Was it difficult or easy? If yes, why? If no, why?

_____

_____

_____

13.4 A warm/hot meal e.g. *How does it taste? What is the texture like on your tongue?*

How did it feel doing this exercise? Was it difficult or easy? If yes, why? If no, why?

_____

_____

_____

13.5 Swimming in a swimming pool or in a safe river.

How did it feel doing this exercise? Was it difficult or easy? If yes, why? If no, why?

_____
_____
_____

13.6 Taking or relaxing in a nice cold or warm bath or shower.

How did it feel doing this exercise? Was it difficult or easy? If yes, why? If no, why?

_____
_____
_____

13.7 A beautiful fun and relaxing holiday, or doing a puzzle.

How did it feel doing this exercise? Was it difficult or easy? If yes, why? If no, why?

_____
_____
_____
_____

13.8 Being with or gazing at a blossoming flower.

How did it feel doing this exercise? Was it difficult or easy? If yes, why? If no, why?

_____

_____

_____

13.9 Laying on a beautiful beach with the weather not too hot or cold.

How did it feel doing this exercise? Was it difficult or easy? If yes, why? If no, why?

_____

_____

_____

13.10 Walking and noticing your steps or the surroundings.

How did it feel doing this exercise? Was it difficult or easy? If yes, why? If no, why?

_____

_____

_____

13.11 Dancing and noticing your steps or the surroundings.

How did it feel doing this exercise? Was it difficult or easy? If yes, why? If no, why?

_____

_____

_____

13.12 Being in a beautiful garden or at a lake.

How did it feel doing this exercise? Was it difficult or easy? If yes, why? If no, why?

_____

_____

_____

13.13 Watching beautiful waves forming and dispersing in the sea.

How did it feel doing this exercise? Was it difficult or easy? If yes, why? If no, why?

_____

_____

_____

13.14 Watching cars or trains passing.

How did it feel doing this exercise? Was it difficult or easy? If yes, why? If no, why?

_____

_____

_____

13.15 Being with or gazing at the smile of a baby.

How did it feel doing this exercise? Was it difficult or easy? If yes, why? If no, why?

13.16 Gazing at the beautiful clouds floating away.

How did it feel doing this exercise? Was it difficult or easy? If yes, why? If no, why?

13.17 Enjoying, smelling the sweet aroma of and eating a delicious meal.

How did it feel doing this exercise? Was it difficult or easy? If yes, why? If no, why?

13.18 Looking at a river floating away. Looking at the river from a balcon. Sitting near the river.

How did it feel doing this exercise? Was it difficult or easy? If yes, why? If no, why?

13.19 Bird watching.

How did it feel doing this exercise? Was it difficult or easy? If yes, why? If no, why?

13.20 Allowing the flavour and taste of a chocolate bar/sweet candy to slowly drip down your throat.

How did it feel doing this exercise? Was it difficult or easy? If yes, why? If no, why?

_____

_____

_____

13.21 Ironing a shirt and feeling the warmth (do not get yourself burnt).

How did it feel doing this exercise? Was it difficult or easy? If yes, why? If no, why?

_____

_____

_____

13.22 Feel the taste of a lemon/onion.

How did it feel doing this exercise? Was it difficult or easy? If yes, why? If no, why?

_____

_____

_____

13.23 What's next?

Now that you have worked through this section, you should pause and reflect on your answers. Put the book aside for a few minutes before answering the questions below

☐ What have you learned and achieved from this section?

_____

_____

_____

☐ What self-help coping techniques do you want to learn?

_____

_____

_____

☐ Are there any questions you would like to ask medical professionals?

_____

_____

_____

☐ What specific self-improvement goal or achievement do you want to set for yourself for the next week?

_____

_____

_____

It may be useful to provide yourself with at least five minutes twice a week to regularly review and reflect on your self-improvement goal. If you do not set aside time to take care of your wellbeing, the daily demands of life may overwhelm you, and it will become harder to develop self-help techniques.

Do not ignore your well-being because life is not endless here on earth. Try to do at least one small act of kindness, compassion, or self-care for yourself today.

My Review Date _____ **Time** _____ **Place** _____

13.24 Your Feedback.

The Twin Brain Project Team would like to hear from you if you have helpful suggestions that could help them to improve any aspect of this section for other users. Email your suggestions to admin@twinbrain.org. Please copy info@healthbj-uk.org into your email to make sure your feedback is received. Thank you in advance for helping to improve the Twin Brain resource.

Chapter 14
MINDFULNESS TECHNIQUES

This chapter provides you with some mindfulness tools to practise to start living a serene life.

14.1 Mindfulness.

Mindfulness is used to help you be aware of and notice your surroundings and recognise what is happening to you. You do not actively participate in your surroundings: you are a passive participant and must learn to be still.

To do this, you just need to be there and do nothing. Do stop doing what you were doing and just sit there. You do not have to think too hard about it - just be aware of what is happening and do not get involved. Deliberately stop yourself from being drawn into what is going on. **Notice, but do not engage**.

Mindfulness requires you to notice thoughts and worries but watch them coming and floating away - don't engage with them. Be a bystander, be an observer, be there, be aware and be in the moment. It is like drifting on water while using one or two senses to experience the moment. Slow down, get lost, drift away, and become totally absorbed in the moment. **Allow the world to flow by you.**

How true is this for you at the moment? If yes, why? If no, why?

14.2 Benefits of Mindfulness.

- ▶ Emotional serenity, positivity, and happy hormones (serotonin).
- ▶ Gives you an opportunity to find your inner child.

How true is this for you at the moment? If yes, why? If no, why?

14.3 Challenges of mindfulness and attention focusing.

- It takes time.
- Can be difficult to practise.
- Requires patience and persistence.

How true is this for you at the moment? If yes, why? If no, why?

_____

_____

_____

14.4 Practice Guide.

We have used the same examples as above for you to practise Mindfulness. Next time you use these objects or are in these situations, try to follow the Practice Guide and be mindful of what is happening around you.

a). Tea or coffee.

How did it feel doing this exercise? Was it difficult or easy? If yes, why? If no, why?

_____

_____

_____

_____

b). Glass of water.

How did it feel doing this exercise? Was it difficult or easy? If yes, why? If no, why?

_____

_____

_____

c). Kitchen sink and washing plates/dishes.

How did it feel doing this exercise? Was it difficult or easy? If yes, why? If no, why?

_____

_____

_____

d). A warm/hot meal.

How did it feel doing this exercise? Was it difficult or easy? If yes, why? If no, why?

_____

_____

_____

e). Swimming in a swimming pool or in a safe river.

How did it feel doing this exercise? Was it difficult or easy? If yes, why? If no, why?

_____

_____

_____

_____

_____

f). Taking or relaxing in a nice cold or hot bath or shower.

How did it feel doing this exercise? Was it difficult or easy? If yes, why? If no, why?

_____

_____

_____

g). A beautiful fun and relaxing holiday.

How did it feel doing this exercise? Was it difficult or easy? If yes, why? If no, why?

_____

_____

_____

h). Gazing at a blossoming flower.

How did it feel doing this exercise? Was it difficult or easy? If yes, why? If no, why?

_____

_____

_____

i). Laying on a beautiful beach with the weather not too hot or cold.

How did it feel doing this exercise? Was it difficult or easy? If yes, why? If no, why?

_____

_____

_____

_____

_____

j). Mindful walking or working.

How did it feel doing this exercise? Was it difficult or easy? If yes, why? If no, why?

_____

_____

_____

k). Mindful dancing or haircut.

How did it feel doing this exercise? Was it difficult or easy? If yes, why? If no, why?

_____

_____

_____

l). Being in a beautiful garden or at a lake.

How did it feel doing this exercise? Was it difficult or easy? If yes, why? If no, why?

_____

_____

_____

m).Watching beautiful waves forming and dispersing in the sea.

How did it feel doing this exercise? Was it difficult or easy? If yes, why? If no, why?

_____

_____

_____

n). Watching cars or trains passing.

How did it feel doing this exercise? Was it difficult or easy? If yes, why? If no, why?

_____

_____

_____

o).Being with or gazing at the smile of a baby.

How did it feel doing this exercise? Was it difficult or easy? If yes, why? If no, why?

_____

_____

_____

_____

p). Gazing at the beautiful clouds floating away.

How did it feel doing this exercise? Was it difficult or easy? If yes, why? If no, why?

_____

_____

_____

q). Enjoying, smelling the sweet aroma of and eating a delicious meal.

How did it feel doing this exercise? Was it difficult or easy? If yes, why? If no, why?

_____

_____

_____

r). Looking at a river floating away. looking over the river from a balcony. sitting near the river.

How did it feel doing this exercise? Was it difficult or easy? If yes, why? If no, why?

_____

_____

_____

s). Bird watching or playing with an animal.

How did it feel doing this exercise? Was it difficult or easy? If yes, why? If no, why?

_____

_____

_____

t). Allowing the flavour and taste of a chocolate bar/sweet candid to slowly drip down your throat.

How did it feel doing this exercise? Was it difficult or easy? If yes, why? If no, why?

_____

_____

_____

u). Ironing a shirt and feeling the warmth (do not get yourself burnt).

How did it feel doing this exercise? Was it difficult or easy? If yes, why? If no, why?

_____

_____

_____

v). Feel the taste of a lemon/onion.

How did it feel doing this exercise? Was it difficult or easy? If yes, why? If no, why?

_____

_____

_____

14.5 What's next?

Now that you have worked through this section, you should pause and reflect on your answers. Put the book or App aside for a few minutes before answering the questions below

☐ What have you learned and achieved from this section?

Example

I can create calm in myself by practising mindfulness or attention focusing techniques. I learnt various techniques such as watching waves, bird watching, enjoying the aroma of a delicious meal etc.

_____

_____

_____

☐ What self-help coping techniques do you want to learn?

Example

Swimming, increasing the time duration I'm able to keep a tangerine or a sour lemon piece in my mouth before swallowing it etc.

_____

_____

_____

☐ Are there any questions you would like to ask medical professionals?

Example

How do I know which calming techniques would be most effective for me?

☐ What specific self-improvement goal or achievement do you want to set for yourself for the next week?

Example

To book and start my first swimming class on Friday 27 August 2021, at 9am.

_____

_____

_____

It may be useful to provide yourself with at least five minutes twice a week to regularly review and reflect on your self-improvement goal. If you do not set aside time to take care of your wellbeing, the daily demands of life may overwhelm you, and it will become harder to develop self-help techniques.

Do not ignore your well-being because life is not endless here on earth. Try to do at least one small act of kindness, compassion, or self-care for yourself today.

My Review Date _____ **Time** _____ **Place** _____

14.6 Your Feedback.

The Twin Brain Project Team would like to hear from you if you have helpful suggestions that could help them to improve any aspect of this section for other users. Email your suggestions to admin@twinbrain.org. Please copy info@healthbj-uk.org into your email to make sure your feedback is received. Thank you in advance for helping to improve the Twin Brain resource.

Chapter 15
MORE WAYS TO PRACTISE ATTENTION FOCUSING AND MINDFULNESS

This chapter gives you examples of other ways you may experience mindfulness.

15.1 A workplace meeting.

☐ **Attention focusing** Really listen to each person as they speak. Do not just wait to talk: actively listen, try to understand their point, and contribute your ideas. Write down things that interest you. Think about the details.

How true is this for you now? If yes, why? If no, why?

_____

_____

_____

How did it feel doing this exercise? Was it difficult or easy? If yes, why? If no, why?

_____

_____

_____

☐ **Mindfulness** You could go into a meeting early, sit and be mindful by doing nothing. , Just stay there being calm. You could find a space or room where you can sit for a few minutes, your mind not thinking: , just be there and relax until the meeting starts.

How true is this for you now? If yes, why? If no, why?

_____

_____

_____

How did it feel doing this exercise? Was it difficult or easy? If yes, why? If no, why?

_____

_____

_____

15.2 Eating Food.

☐ **Attention focusing** Spend time to feel the food. Examine the food with your tongue, look at the texture of the food, and look at the food in detail before you swallow it.

How true is this for you now? If yes, why? If no, why?

_____

_____

_____

_____

How did it feel doing this exercise? Was it difficult or easy? If yes, why? If no, why?

_____

_____

_____

☐ **Mindfulness** Close your eyes and enjoy the aroma of the food. *How true is this for you now? If yes, why? If no, why?*

_____

_____

_____

How did it feel doing this exercise? Was it difficult or easy? If yes, why? If no, why?

_____

_____

_____

15.3 Watching a Clock.

☐ **Attention focusing** Count the seconds or the minute hands of a clock as it goes around it. Actively think about the colour, make, type of the clock .

How did it feel doing this exercise? Was it difficult or easy? If yes, why? If no, why?

_____

_____

_____

☐ **Mindfulness** Being in the moment with the seconds or the minute hands of a clock. Think about which hand is moving faster or slower and just flow with that hand of the clock.

How did it feel doing this exercise? Was it difficult or easy? If yes, why? If no, why?

_____

_____

_____

15.4 Safely watching waves in the sea.

☐ **Attention focusing** Count the waves. Spend time thinking about the details-like the size, shape, and the colour of the waves. You may notice birds flying overhead.

How did it feel doing this exercise? Was it difficult or easy? If yes, why? If no, why?

_____

_____

_____

☐ **Mindfulness** When you are in the sea, feel your legs, hands, or whatever part of your body is in the water. See the waves forming and coming towards you. Notice them rising from a little shape as they grow up, bigger, bigger. You are not interested in the crowd of people around you or the birds flying overhead. You are not counting the waves. You feel the waves coming and splashing on you. You make no movement or effort, just be there with the waves doing their thing. The waves form shapes. T hey come and pass through you.

How did it feel doing this exercise? Was it difficult or easy? If yes, why? If no, why?

_____

_____

_____

_____

_____

_____

15.5 Picture or Photograph.

☐ **Attention Focusing** Spend time looking at a picture and try to describe every detail on it.

How did it feel doing this exercise? Was it difficult or easy? If yes, why? If no, why?

☐ **Mindfulness** Looking at the picture and stay with it without going into analysis. Meditate on the feeling it gives you.

How did it feel doing this exercise? Was it difficult or easy? If yes, why? If no, why?

15.6 Swimming Safely.

☐ **Attention focusing** You swim in the swimming pool , river, or sea. You are very conscious of your environment You open your eyes, you want to see the bubbles or whatever is in the water. You want to see how dark the water may be or how much light is around you. You count how many seconds you can be under the water.

How did it feel doing this exercise? Was it difficult or easy? If yes, why? If no, why?

☐ **Mindfulness** You are swimming and you do not care about the world around you. You become one with the water. You are not fighting against the water. You float with the water and feel it around you. Feel the cold or warmth of the water.

15.7 Solemn faith/belief practices.

☐ **Attention focusing** You are an active participant experiencing the presence of the divine or supernational in a place or house of worship. You sit, stand, or stay in a body position (permitted by the local rules). . You may be there alone or in a group. The environment should exhibit stillness, silence, soberness, awe-inspiring etc. You stay very conscious of using each and all your five senses (if possible) to interact with and become one (unity) with the place or house of worship and the divine or supernational entity you believe in and worship. For most major religions this entity is 'God' with a big letter 'G' and for others , this entity is 'god' or 'gods' with a small letter 'g'. Anything they believe including having no belief or believing in oneself, a political philosophy or a profession. ***Note you have a right and a choice to have 'no belief' and other people have the right and choice to have a belief.***

In the faith/ belief-based attention focusing, you may open or close your eyes. You can make a deep or a light personal conversation with your divine or supernational entity. You silently present, share or negotiate each item on your agenda- the love you receive and give, mercy and favours granted you or you want to receive, flaws you like to overcome, other people need you like to intercede for etc. You may not have a specific list of items to converse about, but a space to let your divine or supernational entity know how pissed off, frustrated, stressed, or tired life is for you or about something that happened to you or someone else. Or you may spend the time going through the list of every good thing you are thankful for.

Or you may choose not to engage in a conversation, but spend your time looking, examining in detail, and connecting with each solemn and awe-inspiring object or experience in the place or house of worship. Example, the photos and images handing, candles burning, architectural design, people around you engrossed in silent worship. If it is an open worship environment surrounded by nature, you may look around and get engrossed being thankful for the birds singing, animals you see doing their own daily routine activities, etc.

How did it feel doing this exercise (if applicable to you)? Was it difficult or easy? If yes, why? If no, why?

_____

_____

_____

☐ **Mindfulness** You are there as a passive participant experiencing the presence of your divine or supernational entity in the place or house of worship. You are in the solemn awe-inspiring place or house of worship and you do not engage or take any notice of the world around you. You use one or few senses (if possible) to connect and interact with and become one (unity) with the divine or supernational entity you believe in and worship. You are not examining details and going over a list of items to share or present. You listen to be spoken to, whispered to, be inspired, be touched by and float to and from your divine or supernational entity's presence. You acknowledge distracting thoughts, people, and things around you, but you do not engage, rather you let the distractions float away into oblivion like soap bubble float away and disappears.

15.8 What's next?

Now that you have worked through this section, you should pause and reflect on your answers. Put the book or a pp aside for a few minutes before answering the questions below

☐ What have you learned and achieved from this section?

Example

I can use one thing or object to practise both mindfulness and attention focusing. Example, a workplace meeting or a photograph.

_____

_____

_____

☐ What self-help coping techniques do you want to learn?

Example

Wellbeing benefits of safe swimming.

_____

_____

_____

☐ Are there any questions you would like to ask medical professionals?

Example

Could mindful and attention focusing dancing give similar wellbeing benefits like swimming and other calming techniques?

_____

_____

_____

☐ What specific self-improvement goal or achievement do you want to set for yourself for the next week?

Example

To practise mindful attendance at my next team meeting of Tuesday 31 August 2021, 3pm.

_____

_____

_____

It may be useful to provide yourself with at least five minutes twice a week to regularly review and reflect on your self-improvement goal. If you do not set aside time to take care of your wellbeing, the daily demands of life may overwhelm you, and it will become harder to develop self-help techniques.

Do not ignore your well-being because life is not endless here on earth. Try to do at least one small act of kindness, compassion, or self-care for yourself today.

My Review Date ——————— Time ————— Place ———————

15.9 Your Feedback.

The Twin Brain Project Team would like to hear from you if you have helpful suggestions that could help them to improve any aspect of this section for other users. Email your suggestions to admin@twinbrain.org. Please copy info@healthbj-uk.org into your email to make sure your feedback is received. Thank you in advance for helping to improve the Twin Brain resource.

Chapter 16
PLANNING YOUR SAFETY AND KEEPING YOUR RECOVERY

16.1 Your Safety Plan.

a). A free resource on self-harming is available from

https//www.mind.org.uk/information-support/types-ofmental-health-problems/self-harm/about-self-harm/

Note MIND UK acknowledged.

▶ **You may also contact** the crisis help services, your family doctor, your counsellor, a friend, and family members in your country.

b). **Question** What 5 things or situations will trigger you to feel low, to feel like hurting yourself, or, to feel suicidal?

Answer

Example

1. *Someone ignoring me.*
2. *Severe neck pain with doctors telling me there is no cure.*
3. *Stress from increasing job load.*
4. *Debt collectors sending me threatening letters to take me to court.*
5. *No money to pay my bills.*

Write here:
6.
7.
8.
9.
10.

c). Question What methods can you use to keep yourself safe if you feel like hurting yourself or feel suicidal?

Answer

Example

1. *Tell my best friend that I'm feeling crappy, and I need to talk to someone.*
2. *Keep emergency contact numbers on my mobile phone and call my local Crisis Support Agency.*
3. *Go to my local Accident and Emergency hospital department.*
4. *Making sure I don't keep sharp objects or anything I could use to cut myself.*
5. *Create a coping card with self-prompts, such as tips for doing breathing exercise.*

Write here:

6.
7.
8.
9.
10.

d). Question What are 5 positive things to remember when you feel like hurting yourself or you feel suicidal (e.g. religious beliefs, negative impact upon others, being hopeful, etc)?

Answer

Example

1. *It's against my religious faith to commit suicide.*
2. *My family will be in pain.*
3. *There is always a solution to every problem.*
4. *I won't take the easy way out of my problems.*
5. *I have a career and a life ahead of me.*

Write here.

   6.

   7.

   8.

   9.

  10.

e). Question Which 3 people can you contact to support you (e.g., informing close family and friends so they can check-in on me 24 hours, etc)?

Answer

Example:

  1. Your mum.

  2. My best friend.

  3. My housemate

Write here.

   4.

   5.

   6.

f). Question What are your other 3 sources of assistance?

Answer

Example:

  1. sister-in-law.

  2. counsellor.

  3. pastor.

Write here.

   4.

   5.

   6.

g). **Question** Write here the contact details of organisations or people whom you can contact to help you.

Answer

1. *My sister-in-law (Tel +44 (0) 7888888880).*
2. *My counsellor at Chris Therapy Service (Tel +44 (0) 7444444444).*
3. *My pastor at Holistic Wellbeing Outreach (Tel +44 (0) 7333322220).*

Write here.

4.

5.

6.

h). **Question** When is your Safety Plan Review Day and time?

Answer

Example

Date 29 September 2021. **Time** 900am

Write here:

Date Time

16.2 Maintaining Recovery.

To keep benefiting from your recovery journey, you must learn how to face and manage short-term setbacks (lapses) and longer-term setbacks (relapses).

a). **Question** Which 3 of the learned techniques and principles of this resource have you found to be the most useful?

Answer

Example:

1. *'Ask Yourself Technique to reduce stress and anxiety'.*
2. *Breathing exercise.*
3. *Counting numbers and alphabets backward.*

Write here:

    4.

    5.

    6.

  b). Question What 3 things tend to trigger your emotional difficulty?

Answer

Example:

    1. Too much workload.

    2. Excessive heat.

    3. Having to deal with conflicts and arguments with anyone.

Write here.

    4.

    5.

    6.

  c). Question What are the 3 early signs of your emotional difficulty getting worse?

Answer

Example :

    1. Poor sleep.

    2. Migraine/headaches.

    3. Avoiding talking/expressing your feelings when you are really pissed.

Write here.

    4.

    5.

    6.

d). Question Which 2 steps will you take if you notice you are returning to your old thoughts?

Answer

Example:

1. *Talk with the person who pissed me off or my paster or therapist.*
2. *Write out my feelings and solve any problem I'm having.*

Write here:

3.

4.

5.

e). Question Which 3 steps can you regularly make to keep moving forward?

Answer

Example:

1. *Keep practising coping techniques learnt from therapy or self-help sources (e.g., twin brain app or a therapy book).*
2. *Do self-care activities such as swimming, going for a walk etc.*
3. *Good sleep and eating healthy food.*

Write here:

4.

5.

6.

f). Question What are your 3 small step behaviours or actions for the next 7 days?

Answer

Example:

1. *Go for a run-on Saturday at 10am for 3 minutes.*
2. *Visit your parents on Sunday.*
3. *Cook healthy dinner and not eat snacks.*

Write here:

4.

5.

6.

g).Question What are your 3 small step rewards if you can put your small step behaviours into practice for the next 7 days?

Answer

Example:

1. *Watch one of your favourite movies.*
2. *Buy and eat your favourite mango fruit.*
3. *Play computer game for 45 minutes.*

Write here:

8.

9.

10.

17.1 UK Emergency Contacts.

☐ 'I can't find someone to trust or to keep my secrets!' You might not want to talk to a family member or a close friend about things that are difficult or personal. You may not have someone you can trust to keep your secrets. If this is the case and you are struggling with your emotions or you feel like being at risk to yourself or to someone else, you can contact one of the confidential Helplines you know already, or you can try contacting the Helplines below.

Note

▶ Helplines may not be able to assist you if there is a national crisis like an epidemic, a pandemic, a war, or other major disasters.

▶ I accept that this resource gives limited information on Helplines available to me. This resource, Twin Brain Ltd, Health City or Health BJ-UK MUST NOT be used by you as an alternative to crisis support or professional help.

17.2 Helplines for UK Residents.

☐ **Samaritans** *Phone 08457 909090. 24-hour crisis line for people in distress or thinking of suicide. Email jo@samaritans. org. www.samaritans.org/*

☐ **Saneline** *Phone 03003047000, 07984967708. Practical information, crisis care and emotional support. Email support@ sane.org.uk, www.sane.org.uk/*

☐ **Phone your doctor (GP)** *if you must, during your surgery working hours.*

☐ *Search the Single Point of Access (SPA) Crisis Helpline* in your Borough of residence and ask for help 24 hours /seven days.

☐ **NHS Direct 111** *24 hours a day.*

☐ **NHS Phone 111 British Sign Language** *if you require assistance*
- *England – NHS 111 (BSL) interpreter service.*
- *Scotland – NHS 24 111*
- *Wales – NHS 111 Wales*
- *Northern Ireland – NHS 111 Northern Ireland*
- *Or call 18001 111 on a textphone.*

☐ **Carers in Mind** *020 8940 7384, Email carers@rbmind.org. For phone support if you are caring for a person with a mental health problem.*

☐ **Carers support** *0808 808 7777. www.carersuk.org.*

☐ **Emergency 999** *If you are suicidal or about to harm yourself or someone else.*

☐ **Your local Accident and Emergency (A & E) Unit** *If you call 999, the person picking up your call can advise you of the nearest A & E that will assist you.*

☐ **Homeless** *0808 800 4444. www.homeless.org.uk/*

☐ **MIND mental health charity** *0300 123 3393. www.mind.org.uk*

☐ **CHILDLINE** *0800 1111. www.childline.org.uk/*

☐ **Alcoholics Anonymous** *0845 769 7555. Website http//www.alcoholics-anonymous.org.uk/.*

☐ **No Panic – Helpline phone 0808 808 0545**. *Helps victims of panic attacks, phobias, obsessive-compulsive disorder, anxiety, and people withdrawing from tranquillisers. Email ceo@nopanic.org.uk, www.nopanic.org.uk*

☐ **Citizens Advice Bureau** *phone 01392 425 517. wwwcitizensadvice.org.uk/.*

☐ **Cruse Bereavement Care** *http//www.cruse.org.uk.*

☐ *Rape Crisis England and Wales* 0808 802 9999. *http//www. rapecrisis.org.uk.*

☐ *Bristol Crisis Service for Women (BCSW) – Helpline 0117 925 1119.* *Supports women in distress and self-harming.*

☐ *Support Line 0208 554 9004.* *Offers emotional support to people of any age on any issue and giving information on available local services. Email on infor@supportline.org.uk.*

☐ *42nd Street – Helpline 0161 832 0170.* *Offers mental health support and advice around suicide and self-injury to young people aged 14 to 25 in Manchester.www.fortysecondstreet. org.uk*

☐ *Nightline (for University students)* *National organisation of NightLine student helplines in Universities across the UK. See its website for the type of assistance offered in your University (if any) www.nightline.ac.uk*

17.3 Overseas Emergency Contacts.

☐ 'I can't find someone to trust or to keep my secrets!' You might not want to talk to a family member or a close friend about things that are difficult or personal. You may not have someone you can trust to keep your secrets. If this is the case and you are struggling with your emotions or you feel like being at risk to yourself or to someone else, you can contact one of the confidential Helplines you know already, or you can try contacting the Helplines below.

Note

▶ Helplines may not be able to assist you if there is a national crisis like an epidemic, a pandemic, a war, or other major disasters.

▶ I accept that this resource gives limited information on Helplines available to me. This resource, Twin Brain Ltd, Health City or Health BJ-UK MUST NOT be used by you as an alternative to crisis or professional help.

17.4 Helplines for Overseas residents.

Contact your friends, family members, and your local Accident and Emergencies in your country.

17.5 Alternatives to Self-Harm Techniques.

Harming yourself may involve pulling your hair, cutting your arm, etc. to cause pain to yourself or to release stress or frustrations.

There are tips to help people deal with self-harming behaviours. You may find some of the tips useful or not useful.

▶ **A free resource available from**
  https//www.mind.org.uk/information-support/types-ofmental-health-problems/self-harm/about-self-harm/

  Note *MIND UK acknowledged.*

▶ **You may contact** the crisis help services, your family doctor, your counsellor, a friend, and family members in your country.
▶ **You may contact** the crisis help services, your family doctor, your counsellor, a friend, and family members in your country.

Chapter 18
SHARING AND HELPING YOURSELF AND OTHERS

18.1 Helping others.

Would you like to recommend an exercise or a specific part of the content of this resource to your doctor, counsellor, friend, partner, or peers in a self-help support group?

Answer If Yes, please write here all the email addresses or mobile phone numbers separated by a comma.

_____

_____

_____

Answer If yes, send each person the website www.twinbrain.org.

18.2 Should I get more medical help?

It is up to you to decide whether you require and need more help after reading and using any of the Twin Brain self-help coping resources. If you are unsure about requiring medical assistance, please consult your doctor.

18.3 Where do I get help?

You may acquire coping techniques from

▶ The self-help guides in *the Twin Brain mobile Apps or web a pps* at www.twinbrain.org or on the Health BJ-UK website at www.healthbj-uk.org. *These tools do not substitute medical advice and care from a trained medical professional.*

▶ Professional support through your family doctor or your trained and accredited local counsellor or therapist. These medical professionals may charge you a service fee for their treatments using their own techniques, or for assisting you to work through the Twin Brain's self-help coping resources.

We do not recommend or endorse any specific professional, but

☐ If you live in the UK, you may contact your doctor (GP) or local NHS Service on how to receive support from a local NHS accredited counsellor or therapist at a low-cost or free.

☐ If you live outside the UK and you know how to find an accredited local counsellor or therapist in your country, you may contact them.

☐ If you live outside the UK and you do not know how to find a trained and accredited local counsellor or therapist in your country, you may contact your local family doctor, to advise you on finding an accredited local therapist near you.

☐ If you are not sure or are unable to get help from the above options, then you may find a trained and an accredited therapist or a counsellor at

▶ **Health City** or **Health BJ-UK** for face to face or remote video, email, chat, or phone counselling or therapy.

Health BJ-UK or Health City
Tel 0333 800 3006 or 0333 789 0012
Email info@healthbj-uk.org or info@healthcity.org.uk
Website www.healthbj-uk.org/ or www.healthcity.org.uk

☐ The Directory of Free, Low Cost or Discount Wellbeing Services on Health BJ-UK (www.healthbj-uk.org) or Health City (www.healthcity.org.uk).

Online Services

You may book remote phone, email, texting or video consultations, counselling, or a therapy from anywhere in the world. Contact your local family doctor or counsellor first for remote support. If you cannot get help locally, you may book remote sessions at www.healthbj-uk.org. You may also search Online accredited Counsellors or therapists offering remote support.

Where to find further details

If you wish to get more familiar with or use more of the Twin Brain coping resources, please visit www.twinbrain.org

Twin Brain
Davenport House, 16 Pepper Street, Canary Wharf, London E14 9RP United Kingdom. Email admin@twinbrain.org
Phone 0333 800 3006, 0333 789 0012
www.twinbrain.org

Chapter 19
OTHER TWIN BRAIN RESOURCES

19.1 How Do I Obtain the Resource?

Available

▶ As books at www.twinbrain.org or www.shop.healthbj-uk. org or other good online shops.

▶ As topics or modules in the *Twin Brain mobile apps or web apps* at www. twinbrain.org.

19.2 List of Book and App Resource.

a). Book One: Do I Have a Protective Twin Brain? or a Module in the Twin Brain App.

The contents include:

▶ **Do I Have a Twin Brain?** The human brain behaves like a computer capturing and storing much information as good or corrupted files. The human brain behaves like a real human being with the ability to use the stored information to help us decide whether to fight or run from threats or to be happy and creative. If files were installed in the brain, good files could be deliberately activated, and corrupted files could be deliberately un-installed, repaired or modified to enable us to live more resilient and fulfilled lives.

▶ **The Twin Brain's Framework for Coping Techniques:** These are suggestions or a brief map on how to plan and progress through your self-help care using the *Twin Brain app* or books. The suggestions are not alternatives to seeking help from a trained medical professional.

b). **Book Two: Coping Techniques for Helpful and Unhelpful Thoughts or a Module in the Twin Brain app..**

Contents include:

▶ Revisit Step by Step exercise to identify your common Corrupted Brain Files.

▶ The Pros and Cons Technique.

▶ The Quick Check with Complete and Accurate Facts.

▶ The Smart Thought Court Technique.

▶ Additional Thought Techniques for Unhelpful Thinking.

There are other techniques that may help you to address or cope with unwanted thoughts. For example, remind yourself that thoughts are not realities, and that thinking does not make thoughts real or bring them into existence unless you actively seek to do it. Do not poke or play with your brain files that behave like the unwanted and irritating pop-up advertisements on a computer's screen. These pop-up brain files are called "automatic thoughts" by health workers. If you keep on poking a thought you are worried about, eventually you might set off an emotion (example, upset, sadness) and turn it into reality. In other words, by worrying about a certain thought, you may end up turning it into existence, even if it has not existed before.

The Twin Brain is teachable. This means that there are proactive steps that you can take to acquire coping techniques and to manage helpful or unhelpful brain files.

c). **Book Three: The Growing Mindset Coping Techniques or a Module in the Twin Brain app.**

Contents include:

▶ The 'Ask Yourself' technique to reduce anxiety and stress.

▶ Quickly Change the Way You See a Situation.

▶ **The 'Magical' Thinking Technique.**

The Magical Thinking Technique suggests that humans can transform positive or negative thoughts into existence. This is different from the daily routine of thinking that keeps our lives going, and keeps us doing our jobs, or going to school. It is also different from the worst-case scenario safety thinking that the Twin Brain uses to protect us from threats. It seems that the human brain has consciousness or is a conscious being and the body is a vehicle only *(McCabe and Selemo, 2020)*.

▶ **The Best Case Scenario Thinking Technique.**

The Best-Case Scenario Thinking Technique sees a problem, a mistake, or a failure as a challenge, a gap, or an opportunity to grow *(Yashkumur and Selemo, 2020)*. It is the opposite of the Worst-Case Scenario Thinking that sees a problem, a mistake, or a failure as a threat and make you start everything from a perspective or point of anxiety and hopelessness. If having worst case scenario thoughts are possible and real, then best-case scenario thoughts are also possible and can be made real. Stress hormones may be released because of the worst-case scenario or the magical negative thoughts.

Happy hormones (serotonin) may be released by having the routine of positive or magical positive thoughts.

d). Book Four: More Coping Techniques for Emotional Resilience).

Contents include:

▶ **Sense Making of your Situation/Condition**

▶ **The Timeline Technique.**

▶ **Complex Brain Files that cannot be quickly repaired?**
The Twin Brain is teachable and there are proactive steps to acquire coping techniques. But some brain files called schemas, extreme rules of loving, extreme core beliefs, or similar, may not be easy or at all repaired or deleted through self-help techniques alone. This is because these are complex files that are not simply stored historical data in the Twin Brain. These complex files are embedded or have become integrated with the computer operating system of the Twin Brain. You require the assistance of a trained medical professional to help or guide you to identify, explore and re-structure these files. The guidance or help of

a professional ensures that the computer operating system of your Twin Brain does not end up damaged during the process, in which you are applying a self-help technique, or getting assistance from an untrained person.

▶ The Extreme Expectations/Rules Technique for Complex Brain Files.

My Way or No Way' attitude or rules are expectations, standards, values, dos', and don'ts. We learned them from our families, schools, friendships, workplace, social and faith groups, and our society. Rules influence the way we behave. They are rigid and their violation is associated with distress. For example, the parental rule for a child not to touch boiling water or hot gas cooker top comes with the consequence of getting burnt if the child breaks this rule. Unhelpful rules cause distress to the person making the rules and those around them because they are unrealistic, excessive, too demanding, unreasonable, and difficult to keep. These rules come with absolute words such as 'must', 'if', 'should' . For example, "If I can't do something perfectly, it's not worth doing it at all". 'I can't tolerate seeing papers and clothes everywhere in the house'. Good or helpful rules support us and the society to live safely, better, and healthier because these rules are attainable, flexible, and easier to keep.

▶ The Theory A, B and Problem-Solving techniques.

It offers you two possible views or options on how to address anxiety or solve a problem. It is either a problem that has happened before and there is a real fear or concern that it may happen again in the future, or it is a problem that has never happened before, but it is of concern and speculation of the worst-case scenario. If a problem is real and has a practical solution, take minor steps, or set up a hierarchical order for solving the problem. If a situation looks like a real problem, but it has not happened yet, or it may occur in the future, or it is out of your control, then stop investing hours solving the problem in your head. A problem that has not existed yet or seems to be distant may never become a reality.

▶ **The Anti-Bullying and Harassment Tools.**

Bullying and harassment are attempts to break the victim's wellbeing and to take emotional power over the victim to cause fear and distress to them. A bully is a cruel and evil person with a broken inner mind and a lack of inner peace. A bully is a sick person, insecure, and has unstable mental health. Bullying and harassment in all forms may cause, contribute, or trigger emotional injury (trauma), disrupt physical health, sleep, appetite, concentration, performance, relationships, low self-esteem, low self-confidence, etc. The technique may help to offer victims a reporting tool to report the bully anonymously, to ask for assistance, or to attend anonymous online forums to share their experiences, read other victims' experiences and to access support resources.

e). **Book Five: Who is Taking My Tea Bags? Subtitle: Self-esteem and Self-Nurturing Techniques) or a Module in the Twin Brain app**.

Contents include:

▶ **The Tea Bag Imagery Technique.**

One of the key techniques is to talk about feelings to clarify thoughts, and to solve problems early and safely take small steps. The question is do I allow procrastination or the worry and fear of making a mistake and being judged by people, stop me from expressing how I feel or from having my needs met? Am I afraid of losing a relationship so much that it leads me to the point of not expressing how I feel neglected or whether my needs are not met?

▶ **The Self-Esteem Re-Branding Techniques.**

What does self-esteem mean to you? Some people may see it as the capacity of loving yourself or appreciating yourself without being narcissistic or arrogant. There are practical steps that can be taken to increase your low self-esteem or to improve upon your existing good self-esteem. For example, remind yourself of the law of self-fulfilling negative prophecy. Part of your brain is human: another part of it is a computer and it may 'hear' your negative words and may learn from it, such as 'I'm ugly, not good enough'. If you keep telling yourself or allow someone to keep telling you negative words, you will end up feeling negative.

▶ **The Increasing Soothing Regulation Bubble Technique.**

The contents help you to look after yourself and be kind to yourself.

▶ **The Cultural Values and Faith Techniques.**

What do faith and cultural value mean to you? Cultural value and faith will mean nothing to you if you do not have any beliefs or specific cultures you call your own. You have the right not to have a belief and others have the right to have a belief. The question for those who have a good belief or good cultural values:

- ➤ do those beliefs and values help you to live a more balanced daily life?
- ➤ do they help you to cope well when there is no further scientific help available to you?
- ➤ do they help you to cope along with available scientific help?

The information shared in this resource is not intended to make the reader convert to the religion of the persons mentioned in the resource. You must make your own judgement and you are responsible to appreciate or reject the received information. For example, *Briege McKenna, the faith healer that baffles medical doctors and the science world.*

http://sisterbriege.com/Universe/Universe.html

f). **Book Six: The Calming, Gratitude, Appreciative Enquiry Techniques or a Module in the Twin Brain App.**

Contents include:

▶ The Appreciative Enquiry (AI) and Problem-Focused questions technique.

▶ Additional Appreciative enquiry questions.

▶ Understanding the Gratitude/Appreciation journal technique.

- The Mobile Gratitude/Appreciation journal.
- The Daily or Weekly Gratitude journal.
- My Appreciation Book.
- Aspirational Gratitude journal.
- The Calming Techniques.
  - Calming Techniques Part One.
  - Calming Techniques Part Two.

The Gratitude/Appreciation Journal Technique.

This helps you allow yourself to be thankful for what you have. To appreciate yourself, others, and your environment. To believe and reward yourself. To show compassion and kindness to yourself. To invest in thinking and doing nice things for yourself without neglecting people who need you. The positive emotions and physical reactions (joy, contentment, calmness, etc.) you feel during the period of showing yourself gratitude or appreciation may link to the release of happy hormones (serotonin) in your body. Serotonin produces many emotional and medical benefits that include reducing anxiety by producing calmness, and increasing the strength of your immune system, and slowing aging.

The Calming Techniques.

By creating calmness, helps to improve the quality of sleep, reduce anxiety, and reduce the replaying of unhelpful trauma (emotional injuries) memories. A few examples (a) counting numbers and alphabets backward: (b) rhythmical breathing.

g). **Book Seven: Techniques for Helpful and Unhelpful Emotions.**

Contents include

The Protective, Drive and Soothing Regulation Bubbles Technique.

The Regulation Bubbles technique has been taken from the research and work of Depue (2005) and Gilbert (2005). Depue described protective threat , excitement and resource-seeking drive system, and safeness-contentment and soothing emotion regulation systems.

The question is how balanced your three motive or emotion regulation bubbles or states are. You may be living your life in one of the three bubbles. These are the Drive Bubble (e.g., pursuing achievements), the Threat Bubble (e.g., worrying, anger), and the Self-Soothing Bubble (e.g., safe, compassionate to self). A lifestyle with a big Drive Bubble or a big Threat Bubble, but with a low Self-Soothing Bubble is not likely to increase your self-esteem or long-term mental wellbeing. Some balance between the Drive Bubble and the Soothing Bubble, but low Threat Bubble could contribute to developing and improving positive self-esteem and mental wellbeing.

▶ The Pleasant and Unpleasant Emotions Technique.

An emotion may be considered as the language that your Twin Brain speaks or is trying to tell you that something is right, uncomfortable, or wrong inside or outside your body. Then it (brain) motivates or pushes us to do different things or to act and respond to the situation that set off the emotion. For example, the Twin Brain uses anger to tell you that something is unfair or unjust. Excitement is used to tell you that something nice has taken place or is currently happening. Being able to feel an emotion means emotions are available to you, and you can experience them. For example, 'I feel angry' or 'I feel loved'. Emotions are not yours to shut down, to avoid or to suppress. However, no matter how painful or difficult an emotion may be, it is there to be expressed or released safely by using proactive steps.

▶ The 'Clinical Forgiveness' or 'Letting Go' Technique.

The technique involves undertaking a challenging, but healing emotional journey, and arriving at a point of recognition and acceptance when you realize that the feeling of 'unforgiveness' (blame) -whether done to you by yourself or by someone else - is like having heavy emotional bricks or chains on your shoulders or in your heart. The suffering is felt by one person only, and that is you. Not letting go of your bricks is like someone flogging themselves expecting someone else to feel the pain. Your brain is investing a lot of capacity of its resource to keep your pain suppressed. If you were to assist your brain to release the resource and capacity it is currently using to carry your emotional bricks or chains around, perhaps your life could have been brighter. Letting go does not substitute the need for seeking justice.

h). Book Eight: One Small Step to Change or Create a Big Behaviour.

Contents include

▶ Barriers To Doing or Changing a Behaviour.
▶ Small Step Actions Technique.
▶ Small Steps Behaviour Experiment Technique.
▶ Brief Behavioural Experiment.
▶ Detailed Behavioural Experiment.

The Doing or Changing a Behaviour Techniques are also called 'Behavioural Experiment'. The techniques are about designing, creating, and carrying out an experiment or a test to help you to

(a) take practical small step actions to try, test or put into practise your new or modified helpful thinking style or behaviours that you have identified already.

(b) check if your positive or negative predictions on the outcome of the experiment shall come to pass or not: and

(c) translate your identified practical small step actions into life skills or a new lifestyle.

i). Book 9: Freedom from being Hurt by Your Past. Subtitle: Forgiving or 'Letting Go' may not Replace Fairness or Justice.

The technique involves undertaking a challenging, but healing emotional journey, and arriving at a point of recognition and acceptance when you realize that the feeling of 'unforgiveness' (blame) whether done to you by yourself or by someone else is like having heavy emotional bricks or chains on your shoulders or in your heart. The suffering is felt by one person only, and that is you. Not letting go of

175

your bricks is like someone flogging themselves expecting someone else to feel the pain. Your brain is investing a lot of capacity of its resource to keep your pain suppressed. If you were to assist your brain to release the resource and capacity it is currently using to carry your emotional bricks or chains around, perhaps your life could have been brighter. Letting go does not substitute the need for seeking justice.

j). Book 10: Thought Court Exercise for Complex Brain Files: This book presents a Thought Court to assist in dealing with complex unhelpful thinking styles or brain files. Remember that complex brain files require a professional assistance to address them.

k). More-help resource are available from: www.healthcity. org.uk/En/Clinical-Resources/

l). Other Self-Help Resource on Twin Brain or Health BJ-UK websites.

The websites are www.twinbrain.org and www.healthbj-uk. org.

19.3 The Emotional Health Self-Screening and Report.

This is a confidential facility on the Twin Brain's psychological assessment website (https://psychassessment.twinbrain.org/ services/emotional-health-self-screening).

This facility gives you a chance to:

▶ Complete popular mood questionnaires such as PHQ9 for depression, GAD7 for anxiety and other essential psychological questionnaires. The questionnaires are free to complete, and you see your scores and interpretations. You may use the facility as a sort of **Mood Tracker and Alert**, where it may use your self-reported anxiety and depression/mood symptoms to help monitor your emotional state. Your mood tracker is expected to alert you and your family doctor (if any) for immediate assistance should your mood scores indicate a reason for concern.

- Gather some information about the challenges or difficulty you are facing and for which you want to seek the assistance of or direct treatment by a trained medical professional.
- Create your screening report for you that you can keep for yourself or send a copy to your health professional who is treating you.
- Reduce the time that would have been spent by your medical professional and you to conduct your first consultation or assessment appointment. Your self-screening report may (though not always) reduce some of the assessment information your health professional would have asked you. This is because a lot of or some of the initial information that your professional wants to know about you will be on your screening report.

19.4 The Free Psychological Self-Assessment Questionnaires.

These are available on the Twin Brain's psychological assessment website(https://psychassessment.twinbrain.org/services/free-self-assessment). You have a chance to complete any questionnaire of your choice or recommended by your health professional. Scores are generated and can be emailed to your family doctor and other healthcare professionals chosen by you. The questionnaire include depression, anxiety, phobia, alcohol use, self-esteem, etc. Use of a questionnaire is intended as a guide only to inform assessment and therapy with your trained medical professional. High scores are not a confirmation of a diagnosis.

19.5 The Coping Techniques Blueprint.

This is a menu in the Twin Brain app (www.twinbrain.org). The Blueprint is on the Twin Brain mobile app and the web app. The Blueprint may help you to:

- Remember to integrate your specific coping techniques into your daily personal lifestyle and your work life. It may help you to bring all the specific coping techniques you have acquired together into a single document including those that you want to acquire from the different sub menus of the *Twin Brain mobile app* or the web app, from the Twin Brain books, or any other techniques you have found useful from elsewhere.

▶ Present your specific coping techniques under key headings for easy practice and self-reflection, for example, changing unhelpful thoughts, rebranding low self-esteem, self-forgiveness, gratitude journal, life and career goals, strategic directions, etc.

▶ Review, edit, update, and save the latest versions and to archive the old version of your Techniques Blueprint up to 3 months (from the date you commenced your first version of Techniques Blueprint) in the *Twin Brain mobile app* or web app. You can email, download, and print copies of your Techniques Blueprint.

19.6 The Directory of free, low cost or discount Wellbeing Services.

This is a search facility in the Health BJ-UK Directory of health professionals (www.healthbj-uk.org). It helps anyone who require it to search for health professionals who offer free, low cost or discount wellbeing services globally. Wellbeing service providers are counsellors, cognitive behavioural therapists, psychologists, psychotherapists, medical doctors, coaching, fitness gyms, medical doctors who provide talking treatments, nutritionists and many more.

Chapter 20
SOURCES, REFERENCES AND ACKNOWLEDGEMENT

Note

Where we have drawn on materials on the work of other people, we tried our best to reference the relevant sources. We do ask that you inform us soonest (admin@twinbrain.org) to help us put right any breach of copyright or if you think we omitted to acknowledge a given work and its author.

You can help to email us any reference source you believe is relevant to any contents of this Twin Brain resource. Thank you in advance.

Adams, A. (2021 August 21). *The Observer Consciousness Interview. Neuroscientist Anil Seth* 'We risk not understanding the central mystery of life'. Retrieved 24 August 2021, from https//www.theguardian.com/science/2021/aug/21/neuroscientist-anil-seth-we-risk-not-understanding-the-central-mystery-of-life.

Barrett, L. F. (2020, November 19). *People's words and actions can actually shape your brain — A neuroscientist explains how.* ideas.ted.com.https//ideas.ted.com/peoples-words-and-actions-can-actually-shape-your-brain-a-neuroscientist-explains-how/

Beck, A. T. (2016). Cognitive therapy Nature and relation to behaviour therapy–Republished article. *Behavior Therapy*, 47(6), 776-784. https//doi.org/10.1016/j.beth.2016.11.003

Bennett-Levy, J., Butler, G., Fennell, M. J. V., Hackmann, A., Mueller, M., & Westbrook, D. (Eds.) (2004). *The Oxford handbook of behavioural experiments*. Oxford Oxford University Press.

Drazba, E. (2020, August). Magical Thinking to Grow Mindset. *Live Therapy Treatment* [Symposium]. Treatment sessions of the Health City, London, UK.

Dugas, M. J. (2004, September). *Manual to accompany workshop at the 34th EABCT Conference CBT for GAD Learning to Tolerate Uncertainty and Emotional Arousal* [Paper presentation]. Conference CBT for GAD Learning to Tolerate Uncertainty and Emotional Arousal, Concordia University & Hôpital du Sacré-Cœur de Montréal.

Dugas, M. J., Francis, K., & Bouchard, S. (2009). Cognitive behavioural therapy and applied relaxation for generalized anxiety disorder A time series analysis of change in worry and somatic anxiety. *Cognitive Behaviour Therapy*, 38(1), 29-41. https//doi.org/10.1080/16506070802473221

D'Zurilla,T, & Goldfried, M. R. (1971). Problem Solving and Behavior Modification. *Journal of Abnormal Psychology*, 78,107-126

East London Foundation Trust (2021) Appreciative Inquiry. Quality Improvement. Retrieved 25 September 2021, https//qi.elft.nhs.uk/resource/appreciative-inquiry/

Elsevier Patient Education (2020, May 14). *Deconditioning*. Elsevier Inc. Retrieved 16 August 2021 from https//www.elsevier.com/__data/assets/pdf_file/0016/1023622/Deconditioning_140520.pdf#~text=Deconditioning%20refers%20to%20the%20changes%20in%20the%20body,exercise%20program%20in%20which%20activity%20is%20increased%20slowly.

Epstein, N. & Baucom, D. B. (2002). Handout on Emotions taken from '*Enhanced cognitive-behavioral therapy for couples A contextual approach*. Washington, DC American Psychological Association.

Fadok, J. P., Markovic, M., Tovote, P., & Lüthi, A. (2018). New perspectives on central amygdala function. *Current opinion in neurobiology*, 49, 141-147.

Fitch, B. (2010, December 1). Attitudes and Performance. The Impact of Self-Fulfilling Prophecies. *Featured Articles*. Retrieved 16 August 2021 from https//leb.fbi.gov/articles/featured-articles/attitudes-and-performance-the-impact-of-self-fulfilling-prophecies.

Gilbert, P. (2005). *Compassion Conceptualisations, research and use in psychotherapy*. East Sussex, UK Routledge.

Gilbert, P. (2021,13 May). Seeking Permission to Use Your Resource [Image of the Emotion Regulation System]. *Personal email communication from Professor Paul Gilbert* to Health City and Twin Brain Ltd, London, UK.

Greenberger, D. & Padesky, C. A. (1995). *Mind over mood Change how you feel by changing the way you think*. Hove, UK Guilford Press.

Hutto, D. D., and Gallagher S. (2017). Re-authoring narrative therapy improving our self-management tools. *Philosophy, Psychiatry and Psychology*. 2017.24(2)157-167.doi10.1353/ppp.2017.0020.

Jabr, F. (2011, December 8). Cache Cab Taxi Drivers' Brains Grow to Navigate London's Streets. Memorizing 25,000 city streets balloons the hippocampus, but cabbies may pay a hidden fare in cognitive skills. *Scientific American*. Retrieved 16 August 2021 from https//www.scientificamerican.com/article/london-taxi-memory/

Kelly, O. (2020, November 13). How OCD can cause different cognitive distortions in OCD. *Verywell Mind*. Retrieved March 26, 2021from https//www.verywellmind.com/cognitive-distortions-and-ocd-2510477

King, S. (2014) Finding the *Meaning Behind Emotions. Mid Life Moments*. Retrieved March 27, 2021, from https//midlifemoments.me/2014/04/16/finding-the-meaning-behind-emotions/.

Lazovic-Popovicag, B., Zlatkovic-Svendab, M., Durmiccg, T., Djelicdg, M., Djordjevic, S.S., & Zugicfg,V. (2016 May–June). Superior lung capacity in swimmers Some questions, more answers! *ScienceDirect. Revista Portuguesa de Pneumologia (English Edition)*, Vol.22, Issue 3,151-156. Retrieved 16 August 2021 from https//www.sciencedirect.com/science/article/pii/S2173511515001979

Leahy, R. L. (2012). *Overcoming resistance in cognitive therapy.* Hove, UK Guilford Press.

Maguire, A.E., Gadian,G. D., Johnsrude, S. I., Good, D.C., Ashburner, J., Frackowiak, S.J.R., and Frith, D.C. (2000, April 11). Navigation-related structural change in the hippocampi of taxi drivers. PNAS, 97 (8) 4398-4403. Retrieved 16 August 2021 from https//www.pnas.org/content/97/8/4398

Markram, H. (2012). The human brain projects. Scientific American, 306(6), 50-55.

Markram, H., Meier, K., Lippert, T., Grillner, S., Frackowiak, R., Dehaene, S., ... & Saria, A. (2011). Introducing the human brain project. *Procedia Computer Science*, 7, 39-42.

Mathew, S., (2021 July 27). Swimming gives your brain a boost – but scientists don't know yet why it's better than other aerobic activities. *The Conversation*. Retrieved 16 August 2021 from https//theconversation.com/swimming-gives-your-brain-a-boost-but-scientists-dont-know-yet-why-its-better-than-other-aerobic-activities-164297

Martin, W.F., (2013). *Forgiveness is Power, A User's Guide to Why and How to Forgive*. Vermont, USA Findhorn Press.

Mazziotta. J. (2021 April 21). Perfumer Helps COVID Survivors Regain Their Sense of Smell 'It Literally Brought Them to Tears'. PEOPLE.com. Retrieved 16 August 2021 from https//people.com/health/perfumer-helps-covid-survivors-regain-sense-smell/

McCabe, J., & Selemo, B. F. (2020, August). Is our brain a conscious being and our body a vehicle only? A suggestion. *Live Therapy Treatment* [Symposium]. Treatment sessions of the Health City, London, UK.

Mead, E. (2021, May 17). What are Negative Emotions and How to Control Them? *Positivepsychology.com*. Retrieved August 14, 2021, from https//positivepsychology.com/negativeemotions/#~text=In%20terms%20of%20causes%2C%20it%20could%20be%20a,able%20to%20stick%20to%20a%20new%20workout%20regime

Mirea, D. (2011) Third Wave & Related CBT Tools for Working with PTSD. Workshop Resource. Health City London.

Morals, J.A. (2018) Brain of Emotions. Physics & Neuroscience, Princeton University. Quora.com. Retrieved January 27, 2021, from https//www.quora.com/What-part-of-the-brain-controls-emotions-and-how

Mothes, H., Leukel, C., Jo, H., Seelig, H., Schmidt, S., & Fuchs, R.(2007). Expectations affect psychological and neurophysiological benefits even after a single bout of exercise. Retrieved from *Journal of Behavioral Medicine*. Vol. 40, 293–306. Retrieved 16 August 2021 from https//link.springer.com/article/10.1007/s10865-016-9781-3

Neura Library Australia. (2020, October 30). Amygdala. NeuRA Library. https//library.neura.edu.au/schizophrenia/physical-features/brain-regions/amygdala/

NHS. (2019). *Overview - Obsessive compulsive disorder (OCD)*.

https//www.nhs.uk/mental-health/conditions/obsessive-compulsive-disorderocd/overview/#overview.%2Accessed%20 18%20March%202021. Accessed on 18 March 2021

Philpott, C. (2020 September 14). Why some people become super smellers. *Human Body, BBC Future*. Retrieved 16 August 2021 from https//www.bbc.com/future/article/20200911-how-to-supercharge-your-sense-of-smell

Robichaud, M., Dugas, M. J., & Koerner, N. (2012). *Cognitive-behavioral treatment for generalized anxiety disorder From science to practice*. East Essex, UK Routledge.

Rizzolatti, G., & Sinigaglia, C. (2008). *Mirrors in the brain How our minds share actions and emotions*. Oxford University Press, USA.

Rosenberg, M., & Owens, T. J. (2001). Low self-esteem people A collective portrait. In T. J. Owens, S. Stryker, & N. Goodman (Eds.), *Exending self-esteem theory and research Sociological and psychological currents* (pp. 400–436). Cambridge University Press. https//doi.org/10.1017/CBO9780511527739.018

Randy A. Sansone, A.R., & Lori A. Sansone, A.L. (2010 November). Gratitude and Well Being The Benefits of Appreciation. Psychiatry (Edgmont). 7(11) 18–22. Published online. Retrieved August 24, 2021, from https//www.ncbi.nlm.nih.gov/pmc/articles/PMC3010965/.

Salkovskis, P. M. (1997). *Frontiers of cognitive therapy*. Guilford.

Sharp, J. T. (2002). *Examples of Automatic Negative Thoughts (ANTs)*.RetrievedMarch26,2021,fromhttps//www.drhappy.com.au/wp-content/uploads/Examples-Of-Unhelpful-Thinking.pdf

Spiegel, D. (2008). Intelligent design or designed intelligence? Hypnotizability as neurobiological adaptation. *Symptoms based on brain tumour location*. (n.d.). The Brain Tumour Charity. Retrieved March 26, 2021, from

https//www.thebraintumourcharity.org/brain-tumour-signs-symptoms/brain-tumour-location-symptoms/

Stukas, A. A., & Snyder, M. (2016). Self-fulfilling prophecies. In H. S. Friedman (Ed), *Encyclopedia of mental health* (2nd edition, Vol. 4, pp. 92-100). San Diego, CA Academic Press.

Subedi, B. & Grossberg, T.G. (2011, Aug 14). Phantom Limb Pain Mechanisms and Treatment Approaches. *Pain Res Treat.* 2011: 2011 864605. Retrieved 16 August 2021 from

https//www.ncbi.nlm.nih.gov/pmc/articles/PMC3198614/

Sound Media (-). Swimming In the Ocean. *Publicdomainpictures.net*. Retrieved 16 August 2021 from

https//www.publicdomainpictures.net/en/viewimage.php?image=348720& picture=swimming-in-the-ocean. License CC0 Public Domain.

Symphonic Mind Ltd (2007). What Are Brainwaves? *Brain Works*. Retrieved 16 August 2021 from https//brainworksneurotherapy.com/what-are-brainwaves

The New York Times (2013 April 30). Lost Every Day Colorado Woman Has No Sense of Direction. *The New York Times-Bing video*. Retrieved 16 August 2021 from https//www.bing.com/videos/

The Scottish Government (2020 October 09). Relaxation techniques. NHS Inform. Retrieved August 24, 2021, from https//www.nhsinform.scot/healthy-living/preventing-falls/fear-and-anxiety-about-falling/relaxation-techniques.

Timmons, J. (2018, January 4). *When can a foetus hear Womb development timeline*. Healthline. Retrieved March 26, 2021, from https//www.healthline.com/health/pregnancy/when-can-a- foetus-hear

Wells, A. (1997). *Cognitive therapy for anxiety disorders*. John Wiley & Sons.

Wikipedia (2021July 26). Neuroplasticity. *From Wikipedia the Free Encyclopaedia*. Wikimedia Foundation, Inc. Retrieved 16 August 2021 from https//en.wikipedia.org/wiki/Neuroplasticity

Wikipedia. (2001, November 15). *Operating system*. Wikipedia, the free encyclopaedia. Retrieved March 26, 2021, from https//en.wikipedia.org/wiki/Operating_system

Williams, B.(-). *Train clipart*, publicdomainpictures.net. Retrieved 30 July 2021, from https//publicdomainpictures.net/en/view-image.php?image=95420&picture=train-clipart. License CC0 Public Domain.

www.bing.com(...). Adaptation for person born without limbs - Bing video. Bing video. Retrieved 16 August 2021 from https//www.bing.com/videos/s&qpvt=adaptation+for+person+born+without++limbs&FORM=VDRE

Wright A. (2010, October 10). *Limbic system Amygdala (Section 4, Chapter 6) neuroscience online An electronic textbook for the neurosciences | Department of Neurobiology and Anatomy - The University of Texas Medical School at Houston*. McGovern Medical School|Neurobiology & Anatomy. Retrieved March 26, 2021, from https//nba.uth.tmc.edu/neuroscience/m/s4/chapter06.html

Yashkumur, A., & Selemo, B. F. (2020, August). How the "Best-Case Scenario Thinking" sees problems as challenges and failures as fertilizer opportunities? A suggestion. *Live Therapy Treatment* [Symposium]. Treatment sessions of the Health City, London, UK.

Chapter 21
ACKNOWLEDGEMENT AND APPRECIATION

We thank the following people for their past or ongoing motivational, inspirational, or moral support, advice or for helping to review one or more manuscripts. They are listed in no order.

21.1 Motivators, Inspirators and Reviewers.

1. *Jessica Wilson, UK.*
2. *Dr. J. Harrison, UK.*
3. *James Hare, UK.*
4. *Ramat Tejani, UK.*
5. *Michaela Longo, UK.*
6. *Tirza Adebiyi, UK.*
7. *Henry Bodunrin, UK.*
8. *Jade Noble, UK.*
9. *James Dodkins, UK.*
10. *Pui Sue, UK.*
11. *Karen Wilson, UK.*
12. *Sophia Nelson, USA.*
13. *Bruno Afrigana, USA.*
14. *Mary Selemo, Nigeria.*
15. *Ifeoma Onyeaka, Nigeria.*
16. *Naima Ali, UK.*

17. Elzbieta Drazba, Poland and UK.
18. Jennevieve McCabe, UK.
19. Yashkunar Selarka, UK.
20. Lionard Adobor Wikumor, Nigeria.
21. Sonia Osigimo, Nigeria.
22. Dona Azzi, Lebanon.
23. Helen Tonere Yusuf, Nigeria.
24. Godwin & Nancy, UK.
25. Jamie Antwi, UK.
26. Brendan Antwi, UK.
27. Rev. Robert Copsey, UK.
28. Dennis & Mercy Opuofeni, Germany.
29. Bukola Anthonette Ikengboju, UK.
30. Roselyn Fegbe-otu Selemo, Nigeria.
31. Igor Kudobetska, Poland.
32. Mokshesh Kamlesh Kuriya, India.
33. Viviane Gortchenko Ferrari, UK.
34. Arlette L'Olive, UK.
35. Merina Thomas, UK.
36. Willy Kevin Gold-Detchebs, UK.
37. Sukhraj Batcha, UK.
38. Harry Haslam, UK.
39. Anirbed Baruah, London.
40. Kirsty Walker, London.
41. Dr. Hyacinth Oroko Egbebo, Nigeria.
42. Dr. ShamilWanigaratne, Sri lanka.
43. Mary Telford, UK.
44. Anne Afrigana, USA.
45. Gladys Onyeaka Harold-Juwah, Nigeria.
46. Vera Onyeaka-Onyilo, Nigeria.
47. Harold Juwah, Nigeria.
48. And many others.

21.2 Editors.

Sarah Michie: Sarah is from Scotland, UK. She holds a MA (Hons) in Psychology, as well as a degree in Scots Law. She is currently living in London, where she works for a legal tech start-up before starting her legal traineeship in September 2021.

Mohammad Shuja-ul Hoda: Shuja is a cognitive behaviour therapist, an interpersonal therapist, a couple therapist and a trainee hypnotherapist. He has plus 25 years' mental health skills and knowledge working with patients in the UK National Health Service (NHS).

Jacquie Rondon: Now retired, Jacquie worked for 34 years in general and cardio-thoracic intensive care in the United National Health Service (NHS) and private sector: caring for neonatal and adult patients: eventually sister in a cardio-thoracic unit in both sectors during her long career.

L - #0662 - 060622 - C196 - 229/152/11 - PB - DID3322606